THE IMPACT OF THE FOOD AND DRUG ADMINISTRATION ON OUR SOCIETY

CONTRIBUTORS*

HERBERT BLUMENTHAL

VIVIAN R. BOARDMAN

ANNE R. BOURKE

HERBERT A. BRAUN

JOHN T. CAIN

ARTHUR A. CHECCHI

FRANKLIN D. CLARK

JOHN H. COLLINS

NEVIS E. COOK

JACK M. CURTIS

BERNARD DAVIDOW

HARRY F. DOWLING

J. H. DRAIZE

CHARLES WESLEY DUNN

WILLIAM V. EISENBERG

O. GARTH FITZHUGH

JOHN P. FRAWLEY

GILBERT S. GOLDHAMMER

GORDON A. GRANGER

R. L. GRANT

DONALD G. GROVE

E. C. HAGAN

ROBERT A. HARDT

WILLIAM D. HARKNESS

F. LESLIE HART

ALBERT A. HOLLAND, JR.

WILLIAM R. JESTER

IRVIN KERLAN

ERNEST Q. KING

J. KENNETH KIRK

O. L. KLINE

GEORGE P. LARRICK

EDWIN P. LAUG

A. J. LEHMAN

HENRY A. LEPPER

L. M. LUSKY

JOSEPH L. MAGUIRE

McKAY McKINNON, JR.

BRADSHAW MINTENER

LEE W. MINTON

A. A. NELSON

E. M. NELSON

LEO G. PARMER

WILLIAM A. RANDALL

W. B. RANKIN

ROBERT S. ROE

RICHARD SALOMON

L. R. SHELTON, JR.

WALTER F. SILBERSACK

GLENN G. SLOCUM

RALPH G. SMITH

MALCOLM R. STEPHENS

G. CULLEN THOMAS

CHESTER D. TOLLE

ERNEST J. UMBERGER

H. G. UNDERWOOD

FRANK A. VORHES, JR.

BERT J. VOS

FRANCIS X. WAZETER

FRANK H. WILEY

GEOFFREY WOODARD

ROBERT E. ZWICKEY

* The affiliations of the contributors are given in the headings of their respective articles.

THE IMPACT OF THE

FOOD AND DRUG ADMINISTRATION

ON OUR SOCIETY

A Fiftieth Anniversary Panorama

EDITED BY

HENRY WELCH, Ph.D.

AND

FELIX MARTI-IBAÑEZ, M.D.

MD PUBLICATIONS, INC.

NEW YORK, N.Y.

1956

LIBRARY OF CONGRESS CATALOG CARD NUMBER: 56-9328

ACKNOWLEDGMENT

The free distribution of this book as a public service to members of Congress, Food and Drug Administration and public health officials, educational institutions, medical and dental schools, medical and home economics associations, hospitals, and clinics has been made possible through the cooperation of MD Publications, Inc., which has graciously contributed its services, and the generosity of the following food and drug manufacturers:

SPONSORS

AMERICAN CYANAMID COMPANY
Lederle Laboratories Division
Pearl River, New York

MONSANTO CHEMICAL COMPANY
St. Louis, Missouri

CHAS. PFIZER & CO., INC.
Brooklyn, New York

E. R. SQUIBB & SONS
Division of Olin Mathieson
Chemical Corporation
New York, New York

WINTHROP LABORATORIES
New York, New York

ASSOCIATE SPONSORS

BRISTOL LABORATORIES INC.
Syracuse, New York

MEAD JOHNSON & COMPANY
Evansville, Indiana

CONTRIBUTORS

GORDON FOODS INC.
Atlanta, Georgia

NAAS FOODS, INC.
Portland, Indiana

A. H. ROBINS COMPANY, INC.
Richmond, Virginia

SACRAMENTO FREEZERS INC.
Sacramento, California

DIFCO LABORATORIES, INC.
Detroit, Michigan

25204

CONTENTS

IV | FOOD AND DRUG ADMINISTRATION AND FOODS

V | FOOD AND DRUG ADMINISTRATION AND THE LAW

FOREWORD

A healthy nation is a happy nation. Today as yesterday it is the healthy people who most contribute to the progress of mankind. In contrast, those affected by illness have not only suffered physically and mentally but also carried the onerous economic burden that is the tax of disease. For these reasons, it has always been the historical concern of governments to protect the health of the people so that they may live happily and work fruitfully.

"Be useful to the state! Be happy!" were the concluding words of the academic address "The People's Misery: Mother of Diseases," delivered on May 5, 1790, by Johann Peter Frank, the most outstanding figure in the great public health movement of the XVIIIth century. Across time and space this concern for the people's health crystallized in this country in the Food and Drugs Act of 1906, which since then has illuminated the American road to health.

As a tribute to the Food and Drug Administration, which completes fifty years of service to the nation in June 1956, the journals *Antibiotics & Chemotherapy, Antibiotic Medicine,* and the *International Record of Medicine & General Practice Clinics* have published a series of exclusive articles by key members of the Administration covering their various activities and the different facets of their technical work. In addition, several articles have been included from representatives of the food, drug, and cosmetic industries, a practicing physician, a representative of American labor, and an attorney with wide experience in food and drug law.

These articles explain the evolution of the food and drug laws enacted by Congress and describe the enforcement problems that are encountered by this small group of dedicated men. The diversified scientific skills required to insure the safety of foods, drugs, and cosmetics present a majestic panorama of the endeavors and achievements of our Food and Drug Administration, which unfortunately is little known and its functions poorly understood by the "man in the street."

The integration in this volume of these interesting articles depicting the world and scope of the Food and Drug Administration has been made with the hope that greater numbers of consumers will thereby acquire a better understanding of the functions of the "watchdogs" of the nation's food, drug, and cosmetic supplies and their impact on the nation's health and economy.

HENRY WELCH, PH.D.
Director, Division of Antibiotics,
Food and Drug Administration;
Editor in Chief, Antibiotics &
Chemotherapy, Antibiotic Medicine
& Clinical Chemotherapy

FELIX MARTI-IBAÑEZ, M.D.
International Editor,
Antibiotics & Chemotherapy;
Associate Editor,
Antibiotic Medicine &
Clinical Chemotherapy

(Top left) HARVEY W. WILEY, *Chief of the Bureau of Chemistry, U. S. Department of Agriculture, 1883-1912. Former Commissioners of Food and Drugs:* (top right) WALTER G. CAMPBELL, *1927-1944;* (lower left) PAUL B. DUNBAR, *1944-1951;* (lower right) CHARLES W. CRAWFORD, *1951-1954.*

ORIGINAL "POISON SQUAD." *Volunteers from Dr. Wiley's Bureau who served as guinea pigs by eating foods containing various preservatives to determine if these ingredients were harmful.* Front row (left to right): J. S. CLIFFORD, W. S. ORTON, B. J. TEASDALE, E. B. DUDLEY, E. R. McCARTHY. Top row: W. J. JORDAN, F. C. WEBER, H. W. WILEY, J. H. NORTON, J. H. ELDRIDGE, L. M. SMITH.

GEORGE P. LARRICK *Commissioner of the United States Food and Drug Administration of the Department of Health, Education, and Welfare*

I. INTRODUCTION

Leaders of the Food and Drug Administration

VIVIAN R. BOARDMAN

Chief, Editorial Branch
Food and Drug Administration
Washington, D. C.

The papers gathered under this cover were written by members of the Food and Drug Administration and a few close observers in commemoration of the Fiftieth Anniversary of the first Federal Food and Drugs law. The original Food and Drugs Act was signed by President Theodore Roosevelt on June 30, 1906.

To appreciate fully the evolution from a simple beginning to the complex structure of food and drug control today, requires some knowledge of the history of its staff.

Dr. Harvey W. Wiley, who became Chief Chemist in 1883, began with two or three laboratory assistants and a secretary working in a single basement room in the original Department of Agriculture building. Soon the group moved to a separate building—after a laboratory explosion that perturbed the Commissioner of Agriculture (it was not until 1889 that the Department of Agriculture had a Secretary). When the Division was organized as the Bureau of Chemistry in 1901, it numbered less than 40 people.

Dr. Wiley's struggle for the enactment of the first Federal Pure Food and Drugs law lasted 23 years—first in the laboratory where the analytic data were developed and understood only by trained scientists. Then, in the last few years before the law was passed, the struggle took on the aspects of a popular crusade in which its leader earned the title "Father of the Pure Food Law."

Dr. Wiley began administration of the new law with no background of enforcement techniques, no judicial guidance, and only a small staff of trained chemists responsible for all phases of agricultural chemistry. A fair amount of information had been built up concerning prevailing adulterations and misbrandings.

The entire next year was devoted to setting his house in order to work with the new law, a preoccupation also shared by the industries that would come under its control.

Regulations were drafted, civil service examinations held to secure inspectors, and the analytic force augmented. The original group of inspectors numbered 28. As soon as he looked over the new recruits, Dr. Wiley named Walter G. Campbell Chief Inspector—a step that had a profound influence on the course of food and drug control. Mr. Campbell, an attorney by profession, was to prepare the first seizure libel and direct the enforcement work for a longer period than any man in its history.

Dr. Wiley's enforcement years were turbulent up to the time of his resignation in 1912. Not only was there opposition from some segments of the affected industries but also strife within the Department of Agriculture, which resulted in a curbing of many of Dr. Wiley's activities. Despite these factors, an observer of the entire period of Federal enforcement has stated: "All in all, there never was, before or since in so short a time, such an extensive revolution within the food industries as took place between 1907 and 1912. Never since have conditions in the food industries even approached those existing before the pure food law of 1906 became effective." The drug revolution was slower and came largely under the 1938 revision of the law.

After Dr. Wiley's resignation, R. E. Doolittle served as Acting Chief for nine months until Dr. Carl L. Alsberg was appointed Chief Chemist. Dr. Alsberg, a brilliant research biochemist, greatly strengthened the fundamental scientific basis of the Government's operations and also the education of producers to improve their products through scientific controls. Inexperienced in regulatory operations, he soon found that he needed a competent and trusted assistant to direct the enforcement functions. In 1916 he appointed Mr. Campbell Assistant Chief, in charge of regulatory work.

Under various titles and organizational changes, Mr. Campbell directed food and drug enforcement until he retired in 1944. He also served as director of regulatory work for the entire Department of Agriculture from 1923 until 1933. Dr. Charles A. Browne, who was Chief Chemist from 1923 until the Food and Drug Administration was organized as a separate unit in 1927, also directed the research and technologic work and left entirely to Mr. Campbell the administration of the Food and Drugs Act. Mr. Campbell was the first Chief of the Food and Drug Administration and leader of the move for a better law, which was enacted in 1938.

His successor was Dr. Paul B. Dunbar, who had also entered the Bureau in 1907, having just received his Ph.D. in chemistry. He became Mr. Campbell's staff assistant in 1914 and Assistant Chief of the Bureau in 1925. He was the first Assistant Chief of the Federal Drug Administration, and, in 1942, he became Associate Commissioner. This team of lawyer and scientist throughout these years established the sound policies that are still guiding the Federal Drug Administration staff.

When Dr. Dunbar retired in 1951, he was succeeded by Charles W. Crawford, whose 34 years in the organization had been highlighted by liaison work with legislative advisors and members of Congress who sponsored the Federal Food, Drug, and Cosmetic Act of 1938 and by drafting regulations for its enforcement and the formulation of food standards. Appointed as a chemist in 1917, he had served as Chief of the Interstate Division, which formerly directed domestic enforcement activities, and then as Assistant Commissioner and Deputy Commissioner.

His successor in 1954 was the present Commissioner George P. Larrick, who had joined the Federal Drug Administration as an inspector in 1923. Like his predecessor, he was an active participant in the struggle for the 1938 law, with particular responsibility to inform the public of the obsolescence of the 1906 law. He became Assistant Commissioner in 1945, Associate Commissioner in 1948, and Deputy Commissioner in 1951.

This continuity in the service has extended from top administrative officers

12

to laboratory assistants. In January, 1937, there were 47 people on the Federal Drug Administration's active rolls who had been in the old Bureau of Chemistry when the law was enacted or joined it before the end of 1907, the first year of enforcement. Included were the Chief, Assistant Chief, five Division Chiefs, nine Field Chiefs, a number of analysts, inspectors, and clerks, and the cook for the "Poison Squad." The "charter members" have now all retired, but 21 of them are very much alive today. Approximately 25 per cent of the current staff entered the service before these 47 were honored in 1937. We are now in a second generation of food and drug control with most of those now in charge of operations trained by the pioneers.

Not only the Commissioner and his associates but also all of the District Chiefs have been promoted from the ranks of inspectors and analysts. They agree with the man who said, "If we can see farther than our ancestors, it is because we are standing on their shoulders."

Some of the papers in this volume reflect the evolution of the science and art of food and drug regulation in the continuous struggle to keep pace with affected industries and changing conditions. We have come a long way from Mr. Campbell's first handwritten libel to the complicated processes required to present a court case today; from the few analytic methods Dr. Dunbar found when he reported in 1907 to the 1000 page Official Methods of Analysis of the Association of Official Agricultural Chemists published in 1955; from the drugs and their testing methods in the eighth revision of the Pharmacopoeia to those in the fifteenth revision now governing official drugs—in the fields of pharmacology and nutrition not even contemplated in 1906—and from the early reluctant and suspicious attitudes of the industry members who first resisted the law to the acceptance by many of the working principle that the interests of Government and industry are identical. The discussions of today's complex problems in this volume, however, show clearly that Federal Drug Administration recognizes that it is only part way through its evolutionary process.

The Food and Drug Administration of Today

GEORGE P. LARRICK
Commissioner of Food and Drugs
Department of Health, Education, and Welfare
Washington, D.C.

The Food and Drug Administration, or the FDA as it is popularly known, celebrates the fiftieth anniversary of the Federal food and drug law in the United States on June 30, 1956. The FDA of today is therefore a mature, middle-aged organization.

The most important task of this government bureau is to protect consumers against harmful, insanitary, and falsely labeled foods, drugs, cosmetics, therapeutic devices, and the like. The beneficent influence of the law does not, however, extend only to the ultimate consumer. It adds to the assurance of those who use or deal in foods, drugs, and cosmetics that these products are safe and otherwise above suspicion. Thus the physician can depend both on the reputation of the manufacturer and on the knowledge that drugs are subject to the law's standards. Pharmacists, grocers, and dealers in cosmetics have similar assurance. Finally, the Federal Food, Drug, and Cosmetic Act operates to lessen unfair competition. It thus helps make it possible for the ethical manufacturer and dealer to conduct an honest business without fear of being made bankrupt by cheating competition.

The Food and Drug Administration is a small organization, as government bureaus go. The total personnel on July 1, 1955, was 1033 people. Of these employees, 571 are assigned to various cities throughout the United States, where small laboratories are maintained, to make on-the-spot analyses of foods, drugs, and cosmetics shipped in interstate commerce or offered for importation from some foreign country. The remaining personnel are assigned to the technical laboratory divisions and to the administrative offices in Washington.

The task of the FDA is indeed diversified. Its personnel must include scientists who are capable of determining whether a cereal food is contaminated with rodent or insect debris. They must be able to analyze a spinal anesthetic chemically to determine whether or not it is of the proper strength, and bacteriologically to learn whether or not it is free from bacteria. Other scientists must be prepared to certify the safety and potency of antibiotics. The pharmacologic response of new ingredients proposed for use in food, the safety of coal-tar colors, the effect upon the skin of a new ingredient intended for use in a cosmetic, the vitamin content of a breakfast food or an injection must all be ascertained. The Washington laboratories, assisted by the field scientists, also have the important assignment of devising new methods of analysis to deal with new products and practices.

These are but a few of the tasks confronting FDA scientists in Washington and in the field. Thus a wide diversity of scientific skills is employed. Physicians, physicists, pharmacists, veterinarians, pathologists, pharmacologists, bacteriologists, biologists, chemists, microscopists, and others are on the FDA rolls.

Members of the field staff are the eyes of the Food and Drug Administration. Two hundred and fifty technically trained Food and Drug inspectors are responsible for inspection of the output of 90,000 firms who manufacture or deal extensively in products destined for interstate commerce. The factory inspection is the keystone of FDA enforcement. If the inspector finds, as he does in most instances, that the practices of the firm are above reproach, no further attention is given to that firm. If, on the other hand, the firm's output is suspect, then shipments are traced in interstate commerce, samples are collected, and the necessary corrective action ensues.

The basic philosophy of the Food and Drug Administration is to use every proper procedure to try to prevent violations of the law. Efforts are made to disseminate widely to the affected industries knowledge of what the law requires. Often the FDA can supply information concerning the necessary steps to prevent, for example, contamination of foodstuffs with insects or rodents. Whenever an inspector goes through a factory, he tells the management at the conclusion of his visit of violations that he has observed, and he leaves a written report if he observes

14

poor sanitary practices. Thus every effort is made to use education and other means to prevent violations of the law.

Fortunately the great majority of food, drug, and cosmetic manufacturers have a keen sense of their responsibility and subscribe to the philosophy that what is good for the consumer is good for business. This means that the Food and Drug Administration can largely center its regulatory attention on the fringe groups that are either careless or culpable. When significant and substantial violations of the law are uncovered, it is the policy of the Food and Drug Administration to pursue their prosecution with vigor.

The Food and Drug Administration of today stands at the crossroads. The technologic developments of the last decade, the growth in our population, the large increase in the number of food items, the discovery of many new and potent drugs, and the repeated amendment of the law have multiplied the task of the FDA many fold. Its facilities have not kept abreast of its responsibilities. There appears to be a growing realization on the part of the consuming public, and particularly in the affected industries, that a strengthened FDA is desirable not only from the standpoint of the American public but from the standpoint of the industries as well.

The Food and Drugs Act—Past, Present, and Future

ROBERT S. ROE
Associate Commissioner of Food and Drugs
U. S. Department of Health, Education, and Welfare
Washington, D. C.

This year marks the fiftieth anniversary of the passage of the Federal Food and Drugs Act of 1906, the first Federal law dealing generally with the regulation of foods and drugs. The law was enacted after some 25 years of agitation and discussion in and out of Congress. Dr. Harvey W. Wiley, the Chief of the Bureau of Chemistry, was in the forefront of those who advocated Federal legislation, and, when the law finally was enacted, it was assigned to his Bureau for enforcement.

Among the leaders advocating food and drug regulation was Professor E. F. Ladd, then Food Commissioner of North Dakota. Some of the adulterations and misbrandings revealed by Professor Ladd's investigations were reported in a magazine article in 1905. He was unable to find any chicken or turkey in products designated as "potted chicken" or "potted turkey." He noted a wide use of chemical preservatives, such as boric acid, and extensive use in foods of coal-tar dyes. He found that about 70 per cent of the chocolate and cocoa on the market was adulterated with cocoa shell or other substitutes. Reported sales of "Vermont maple sirup" exceeded the production capacity of that state by about 10 times. Many samples of butter revealed extensive adulteration with other fats, such as lard. These types of substitution and misrepresentation, some of which involved the use of chemicals and dyes that might be harmful or deleterious, were among the reasons why Federal regulatory enactment was sought.

During the latter part of the nineteenth century, an industrial society had, to a great extent, succeeded or replaced the agricultural society that earlier had prevailed in this country. With this transition, larger proportions of the populace became dependent upon the general markets for food supplies. Improved transportation facilities, as well as manufacturing and packaging advancements, permitted increased amounts of foods to be distributed over wide areas. Competition in sales and in the development of products created incentives for illegal profits through the debasement of manufactured foods and the mislabeling of those products. It was in this atmosphere and because of these developments that the first Federal law dealing generally with the regulation of food and drugs in interstate commerce was enacted.

The law of 1906 made few positive labeling requirements—in fact, the misbranding provisions were essentially negative in character, simply classing a food or a drug as misbranded if its label bore any false or misleading representation. There was a requirement for declaring on drug labels the presence of certain substances, such as narcotic alkaloids, alcohol, and a few other substances. An early amendment also required the declaration of quantity of contents on packaged foods. Beyond this, however, the law made no requirement for informative labeling, either as to the composition or ingredients of the products, or as to their manner of use or utility. The law did, however, place in the Federal Government a responsibility for investigation and regulation of foods and drugs in interstate commerce, and vigorous efforts were made by the Bureau of Chemistry to carry out this responsibility.

There can be no doubt that the law and its administration were effective in improving the condition of commercial foods and drugs in interstate commerce. The widespread and reckless use of chemical preservatives was stopped, and the public's interest in the problem of preservatives was aroused through the widely publicized activities of the "poison squads"—the young men volunteers on whom some of the preservatives of that day were tested.

The rapid and extensive technologic developments in industry occurring during the first 35 years of this century rendered the Act of 1906 obsolete in some respects, and demonstrated its inadequacy to cope with some of the new problems. A total population of less than 90 million people in 1906 grew by 1938 to nearly 130 million. In 1906, more than 55 per cent of the population was classed as rural, but by 1938 this figure dropped to less than 45 per cent. Thus the regulatory burden under the Federal law was increased by the greatly expanded market for manufactured foods and drugs and by the appearance of a wide variety of canned and frozen foods which resulted from developments and improvements in industry.

After extensive public discussion and consideration by appropriate committees in Congress, the present Federal Food, Drug, and Cosmetic Act was made law in 1938. It replaced the earlier Federal law, retaining and extending most of the original provisions. It brought the whole field of cosmetics under regulation. Among the new provisions that have proved to be important and effective in the consumer interest are the authority for the establishment of food standards, the prohibition of added poisonous or deleterious substances in food unless necessary or unavoidable (in which case a safe tolerance is authorized), the requirement for proof of safety of new drugs before they can be released for distribution, and the positive labeling requirements established with respect both to foods and to drugs.

The 1938 legislation and the amendments that have been enacted have provided improved regulatory tools for dealing with new enforcement problems created by the scientific and technologic developments of the present era.

The pesticide, dichlorodiphenyltrichloroethane, developed during World War II, represented one of the first of a host of new organic chemicals that became of vast importance as pesticides, replacing to a considerable extent many of the older inorganic preparations. These developments in the chemical industry produced many other new compounds, some of which might appear in food products either as deliberate or as inadvertent additions, and many of which form the basis for important new drugs of great potency.

It is evident, however, that these developments will continue and the present law may be inadequate for the future, just as the original Act of 1906 would be wholly inadequate to meet present day requirements. Already the population exceeds 166,500,000, is increasing at the rate of one every 12 seconds, and the proportion of nonrural population continues to grow. The future problems of the atomic age will require that the legislation keep pace as far as possible with scientific advances and, particularly, that the enforcing agency be provided with facilities, including trained manpower, to administer effectively such legislation in the protection of consumers.

The Food and Drug Administration of Tomorrow

BRADSHAW MINTENER

Assistant Secretary
Department of Health, Education, and Welfare
Washington, D. C.

"Tomorrow" could be the turn of the century, when our children's children will be faced with the problems of better foods and safer drugs. Let's leave that to them, for each generation must evaluate its own needs. I cannot forecast how conditions will be in 2000 A.D. any more than Dr. Harvey W. Wiley and his fellow pioneers could prepare in specific detail for the problems of 1956.

Let us concentrate on what needs doing in our day to correct present failings and to provide a sound basis for the foreseeable needs of the future. For this paper, "tomorrow" is the next decade, the period we all hope to watch develop and to which we can make our personal contributions.

As to the deficiencies of the present, the Food and Drug Administration is operating in a postwar world with a prewar purse. Each of us can recognize, from our personal budgets, how frugal a life that would be. But for an agency charged with protecting our daily necessities from defects in a growingly complex economy, it is even more serious.

Our national income has more than quadrupled since prewar days, bringing with it consumers who have turned to "convenience" foods—precooked and otherwise processed away from the home. Even had they not changed their habits, consumers have increased from 130 millions in 1939 to 166½ millions in 1955. Revolutionary industrial changes have occurred during this period in the growing and processing of crops with the use of preparations still not thoroughly explored. Changes have been even more profound in the drug field—with physicians now administering, and thereby saving lives, drugs developed in good measure during this revolutionary period.

Only fundamentally sound regulatory and regulated groups could have survived the situation. Both have "held the line" without chaos or major catastrophe. On a long-range basis, however, this is not good enough for the consumer, who expects the Food and Drug Administration to keep pace with our advancing economy.

I had been a staunch advocate of strengthening the resources and personnel of the Food and Drug Administration throughout my years of association with the food industry. The conviction that this should be done deepened after I joined the Department and gained an inside view. My forecast for the "Food and Drug Administration of Tomorrow," however, is based on the views of 14 private citizens, selected for their interest in civic affairs and their broad knowledge of consumer and industry problems.

This group, sanctioned by Congress and appointed by former Secretary Hobby, made a comprehensive, independent study from February to June 1955, of the scope of the Food and Drug Administration's responsibilities, its adequacy to protect the public welfare, and the resources available to do the job. The Committee's report does not forecast the problems of tomorrow, apart from the previously mentioned dynamic problems of today, that will inevitably increase in line with their present trend.

Fundamentally, the report points out the woeful inadequacies in Food and Drug Administration's resources to meet today's responsibilities, and makes constructive recommendations as to how they may be corrected tomorrow to provide adequate protection for American consumers.

Aiming at five years and setting 10 as its maximum goal, the Committee recommended a three- to fourfold expansion to be carried out gradually, so that it may be absorbed without waste or basic disturbance to current obligations. Annual reviews by a consumer committee task force during and after this period are recommended for evaluation of progress and current public needs.

What are today's needs to be filled by tomorrow's actions? The Citizens Advisory Committee named these: (1) a larger, more diversified administrative staff, with special skills in planning and educational operations; (2) more trained scientists to keep abreast of technologic developments in the industries; (3) more travelling emissaries—to producers and consumers—to teach and learn new methods for achieving better foods and drugs; (4) more attorneys specializing in Food and Drug Administration problems to assist headquarters and field offices; (5) 1000 inspectors (needed right now, the Committee said, but to be absorbed over the several years the current 200 inspectors will require to train and indoctrinate them and put them into effective production); (6) laboratory, clerical, and other personnel to be augmented as rapidly as needed to support increased inspectional pro-

18

duction; and (7) salaries adequate to compete with comparative commercial employment, at both recruitment and retention levels.

These are the recommendations as far as people are concerned. I list them first because the major strength of an organization is in its staff. But good tools are also essential to efficiency. Here, the committee recommended a new model headquarters building that would bring together the administrative and laboratory operations in Washington, and progressive improvements in field facilities, with equipment to keep abreast of new scientific developments.

It also recommended educational tools, such as documentary films, and a variety of popular, nonlegal literature that would help consumers and industries understand how to achieve maximum benefits under the law.

This all may sound like a "utopia" to the Food and Drug Administration staff, which has spent so many years struggling to do so much with so little, but it is a down-to-earth evaluation of what is actually needed, made by representative citizens, experienced men and women, who have made a careful study of what the Food and Drug Administration has and what it needs for the adequate administration of an essential law.

After these changes are put into effect—and I am confident that they will be—the "Food and Drug Administration of Tomorrow" will be geared to explore rich, untried fields toward better foods, drugs, and cosmetics. I look forward to a day when the staff will be adequate to engage in exchanges of personnel with industry, to the profit of the public. Food and Drug Administration technologists could learn a lot in a year's "sabbatical" in a modern factory, and a quality control man from industry who spent a year in the Food and Drug Administration aura would return to his firm almost as a missionary.

I can envision, also, the mutual benefits that would accrue if a college professor of consumer economics joined the Food and Drug Administration educational staff in exchange for a Food and Drug officer to teach his classes in food and drug problems, particularly if the professor were working on a textbook to be used throughout the land.

Such forecasts into the possibilities of the future could go on far beyond the limitations of this paper—but they are not merely visionary. Each is a practical and realizable goal for "The Food and Drug Administration of Tomorrow."

II. FOOD AND DRUG ADMINISTRATION AND THE PHYSICIAN

How the Federal Food, Drug, and Cosmetic Act
Helps the Physician

ALBERT H. HOLLAND, JR.
Medical Director, Food and Drug Administration
Department of Health, Education, and Welfare
Washington, D. C.

Physicians in practice today can prescribe drugs with the knowledge and confidence that they are safe, effective, and essentially as represented by the manufacturer. How does this professional luxury come about? While we in the United States consider these attributes essential, make no mistake—compared with drug standards or lack of them in many other countries, they are a significant luxury. The busy doctor of today can, in large measure, take these things for granted because of the public protection and standards imposed by the Federal Food, Drug, and Cosmetic Act.

Many pharmaceutical firms have enjoyed and will continue to enjoy reputations for integrity and good drugs. Unfortunately, this compliment cannot be universally applied. Therefore, the standards and requirements of the law serve to assure the consumer, be he physician or patient, that all manufacturers meet certain basic criteria. Potency, quality, and purity are fundamental concepts in achieving a reliable national drug supply. No individual physician and few groups could afford to test adequately each supply of each drug purchased for use in their practice. No single individual possesses the variety of scientific disciplines sufficient to accomplish the task. Fortunately, it is not necessary! The full national resources of the Food and Drug Administration stand ready and daily are actively engaged in the task of checking and double-checking drug products and assuring compliance with the law.

Labeling is an equally important aspect of food and drug work that serves to help and to protect the doctor. Today, just by cursory reading of package inserts accompanying many drugs, he has access to a condensate of medical and technical information that permits the safe and intelligent use of the drugs. To obtain this information independently from the literature would require hours and sometimes days of work. No drug can be well used without knowing its indications, contraindications, cautions, usual dosage, route of administration, and other salient features. This information is required of manufacturers as provided by law. So, too, does the law prohibit false and misleading or unsafe labeling.

Another benefit to physicians from the application of this law is the restriction of certain potent or dangerous drugs to professional channels: in essence, the prescription legend. This section of the law categorizes drugs into two groups: those that can be safely labeled for self-medication and those requiring the supervision of a licensed physician. Few would disagree with the concept that unrestricted traffic in all types of drugs is not in the public interest. It is the Federal Food, Drug, and Cosmetic Act that establishes the statutory basis for controlling the distribution patterns of drugs.

The new-drug section of the law, one of the most important, is of tremendous benefit to the medical profession and to the public at large. It requires that each manufacturer of a new drug submit to the Food and Drug Administration certain specified information, including clinical experience with the drug, for review and evaluation of its safety prior to marketing the drug in interstate commerce. This means that the physician can use a new drug with confidence and with relative safety, rather than assuming the risk of early experimental use. It means that the drug, its labeling, and its potency have satisfactorily met the requirements of the Federal law.

Finally, the enforcement activities of the Administration under the law go far toward removing from the market unsafe drugs and obviously fraudulent and phony drugs and devices. While the latter always have a small bevy of untutored, devoted advocates, they cannot be considered in the public interest by men of intelligence and knowledge, nor are they recognized by law.

Yes, the Federal Food, Drug, and Cosmetic Act does help the physician and it helps his patients. Likewise, the continued intelligent, equitable enforcement of the law commands the physician's understanding and cooperation.

The Food and Drug Administration Physician

ALBERT H. HOLLAND, JR.
Medical Director, Food and Drug Administration
Department of Health, Education, and Welfare
Washington, D. C.

"I will use treatment to help the sick according to my ability and judgment, but never with a view to injury and wrong doing." So wrote Hippocrates almost 25 centuries ago. Today the Federal Food, Drug, and Cosmetic Act is but a legal reaffirmation by the Congress of the United States of the fundamental validity of this great physician's teachings. Our present Federal law recognizes the obligation to treat and to help the sick but to do so with drugs of integrity and safety. It is within the confines of this principle that the Food and Drug Administration physician must function. Notwithstanding the varied duties and responsibilities in the Administration, first and foremost the individual is a physician. And so he must remain if he is to play an active role in the medical phases of the administration of the food and drug law.

Contrary to the common belief that working for the government represents a relinquishing of professional stature and prerogatives, the physician in the Food and Drug Administration finds an opportunity for complete fruition of his highest professional ideals and goals. Nor does he lack intellectual stimulation, for he is constantly confronted with all of the newest and many of the oldest drug problems in medicine. Few physicians are privileged to enjoy the great breadth of personal contacts with outstanding investigators and leading medical authorities that routinely befalls the Food and Drug Administration physician. In fact, few physicians are privileged to shoulder the responsibility for the safety and integrity of our nation's drugs.

The work of the Food and Drug physician is diversified in character and content. The horizon of the work extends from new to old drugs, from antibiotics to analgesics, from electrotherapy to electro-quackery, from labels to literature, and from records to research. The establishment of clinical studies in support of court cases and the recruiting of expert medical testimony is a major medical activity. The physician is called upon to work with staff members representing all other functions of the Administration. This provides opportunity for the physician to use his specialized professional training and knowledge and integrate himself into the over-all program of the Food and Drug Administration.

The American pharmaceutical industry is the finest and most progressive in the entire recorded history of the world. As a result of its vigor, a tremendous, challenging task is imposed on the medical staff of the Food and Drug Administration. The work of the physician in the New Drug Branch is perhaps the most demanding and taxing of any in government. The review and analysis of original investigative data present, in themselves, many unique problems. Often it is useless to refer to the standard textbooks of pharmacology, for the information at hand on a new drug is that which will appear in the texts two or more years hence. The translation of animal data and interpretation of the necessarily limited human studies with a new drug impose great responsibility on the physician. He must clearly reach a decision that may affect many lives. The law further requires that such decision be reached within 60 days. This is a short enough time when one considers the complexity of the problems of new drugs and experimental therapeutics.

The physician in the Food and Drug Administration has many satisfying avenues of professional endeavor open to him. His daily decisions affect more people—more patients—than he could otherwise see professionally in a year. The Food and Drug physician rightfully can take pride in his service to his fellow physicians and to his patients—the American public.

"Letter to a Doctor"

DEAR KARL*:

Your request for information on the "grass roots" operations of the Food and Drug Administration is doubly gratifying. In the first place, it is proof that you still make legible notes in your little black book. Further, it reasserts the continuing interest in the protection of people that has characterized your many years of practice in Tarheelia.

The Food and Drug Administration is a small regulatory unit of the Government within the newest Department—Health, Education, and Welfare. It employs about 1000 people, divided between Washington headquarters and 16 field districts located in key cities throughout the United States. About 400 inspectors and chemists staff the field districts and serve as the "eyes and ears" of the Food and Drug Administration in fulfilling its basic enforcement obligation to detect and correct all violations of the Federal Food, Drug, and Cosmetic Act. It is fortunate indeed that, in the 50 years since the Wiley law went into effect, the vast majority of those who produce foods, drugs, devices, and cosmetics have accepted fully their responsibilities to the American consumer, thus permitting our little group to concentrate on the heedless, the careless, and the greedy.

For many years, the Food and Drug Administration has operated under a "project system." Based on experience, on current reports from the districts, and on an evaluation of probable developments, the Food and Drug Administra-

---

* The addressee, Karl B. Pace, M.D., Greenville, N. C., was the recipient of the 1954 General Practitioner's Award of the American Medical Association. The writer, McKay McKinnon, Jr., is Chief, San Francisco District, Food and Drug Administration, Department of Health, Education, and Welfare. Both were raised in Robeson County, N. C.

tion sets up plans that outline generally the work to be done in various fields. Such plans call for attention first to violations involving possible danger to health. Next in order of precedence are those violations offensive to public decency. Any remaining time is devoted to the correction of economic cheats. This planning is essential for uniformity of enforcement; it assures that all consumers, wherever located, receive the same measure of protection under the statute.

A typical district has 10 to 15 inspectors. These men continuously visit areas where raw materials are produced, points where foods are processed and manu- factured, and points where food products are stored. For example, our interest in a food begins where it grows; it may become hazardous through improper use of pesticides. The product is followed to the processing plant to insure that sound material only is used, that plants are maintained in sanitary condition, and that processing and packing practices insure a safe end product. Significant quantities of food become contaminated through improper storage. Thus, inspectors investi- gate warehouses also. Whenever the abnormal or unusual is encountered, appro- priate samples are brought in for examination by the district chemists to confirm field observations. Once illegality is demonstrated, seizure, injunction, or prose- cution actions may follow. Field districts mesh their operations in developing such cases. Food poisoning outbreaks are routinely investigated, with corrective and preventive action where interstate foods are incriminated. Work on foods takes about two thirds of our field time.

Slightly less than the remaining one third of field time is devoted to work on drugs. These figures may vary widely with individual districts. We have a definite interest in source, condition, and "trueness to name" of drug raw materials. Through the years, however, it has proved true many times that the number one hazard in drug production is poor plant control. Such laxity has resulted in mixed identities, improper formulation, accidental substitution, and mistakes in labeling, sometimes with fatal results. Our trained drug inspectors seek out weaknesses in operating procedures and in plant practices that may result in such calamities. This preventive approach has, we believe, paid rich dividends in "accidents that didn't happen" and in improved control procedures.

Many drugs, tremendously useful in treating disease, are restricted by law to sale on prescription only. A large per cent of our drug prosecutions in recent years have stemmed from the illicit sale of such drugs, especially the barbiturates and the amphetamines. Just recently, United States Attorneys in 10 Federal Districts filed, simultaneously, 22 criminal actions against 42 individual defendants. These cases, developed through a year-long undercover investigation by food and drug inspectors, were based on the illegal sale to truck drivers of amphetamine tablets, popularly known as "goof balls" or "co-pilots." You can imagine the potential highway hazard involved when the driver of an "18 wheeler" doses himself past the safe fatigue point. Incidentally, six of those cases were brought in North Carolina.

There are many, many occasions when the general practitioner is in a unique position to further the enforcement of Food, Drug, and Cosmetic laws. I look to the day when distribution patterns of untoward reactions will jell in a matter of hours instead of weeks: when John Doe, M.D., will just naturally pick up the phone and say, "Here are the facts—get going!"

A Citizens Advisory Committee recently completed a survey of the operations of the Food and Drug Administration and, in its report to the Secretary, recommended substantial expansion of Food and Drug Administration forces and programs. (Incidentally, Dr. Harry Dowling of Illinois was a member of that Committee.) Should the recommendations of the Citizens Advisory Committee be acted on favorably, we can proceed into the second half century of Federal food and drug law enforcement, in which there will be more than one food and drug inspector for each 675,000 Americans. Further, if we can carry out the Committee's recommendations on increased educational and informational programs, we can add "consumer awareness" as a powerful enforcement adjunct. I am enclosing a copy of House Document No. 227, the Citizens Advisory Committee Report to the Secretary. It is a highly significant document.

With all good wishes,

Sincerely,
McKay McKinnon, Jr.
Chief, San Francisco District

Encl.—House Document No. 227

The Role of the Physician in the Food and Drug Administration

LEO G. PARMER
Associate Director, Drug and Device Branch
Division of Medicine, Food and Drug Administration
Washington, D.C., and New York, N.Y.

"*Help Wanted:* Physician completely and expertly trained in all branches of medicine and surgery. Able to give advice relating to the use and misuse of all drugs and devices. Must have sufficient knowledge to assist lawyers in preparation of court cases. Willing to travel."

If the Food and Drug Administration were to place a classified advertisement in the newspapers while in search of a Medical Officer, the copy would probably read as just outlined. The result would be that no one physician could possibly qualify for the position. However, as a working unit the Division of Medicine is so constituted as to be able to render an opinion in all fields of medicine and surgery as they relate to food and drug matters. Such opinions are based on either the personal knowledge brought to the Administration by each physician or by the knowledge gleaned by the physician from whatever source he considers necessary. In the latter realm, the Medical Officer may frequently have to travel widely across the country consulting with doctors who are leaders in the particular field under consideration. The result of such an exploration may end with a written opinion by the Medical Officer that is considered the "current consensus of medical opinion."

Besides consulting with experts in the field, the keynote of the Medical Officer's task is "awareness." There are many ways in which he keeps himself aware in medicine. Many of the Medical Officers regularly attend the conferences or clinics of their particular interest. Attendance at medical conventions serves as an additional source of information. One of the most constant and time-consuming tasks is keeping up to date through combing the voluminous medical literature. Besides having available to himself most of the leading published journals, the Medical Officer also has the able assistance of a Research and Reference Branch that, with great rapidity and efficiency, can supply him with the available literature or abstracts on almost every drug subject. The physician armed with both his awareness and his knowledge of what constitutes the consensus of medical opinion is called upon over and over again to render opinions specifically as they relate to all phases of drug and device action. Such opinions must be completely without bias and must rest upon a solid foundation of fact because the Medical Officer constantly keeps one basic fact in mind, namely, that the opinion must be able to stand up in a court of law.

One of the most important tasks that the Medical Officer assumes is preparing court cases. In this phase of his work, he has four lines of duty. The first is preparing the general medical background of the case. This job requires clarification of all the medical aspects to the point where they can be understood and handled by all who subsequently either assist in the case or hear the arguments in the case. Following this, the physician must comb the country for the best possible expert witnesses who can contribute the facts before judges or juries. This job presents many problems. Although theoretically the entire medical and scientific professions constitute a reservoir of experts, it is not a simple matter to determine which of the experts is best versed and recognized in the field involved. Obtaining the services of the expert is difficult because he must be public spirited enough to be willing to leave his work, either in the university or private practice, and to travel off to some distant city, with little in the way of remuneration. The cooperation of such deputy medical officers is part of the backbone of the Medical Division and explains how the Medical Officers can act so efficiently despite their small numbers.

The third phase of preparation for court involves a joint effort with representatives of the Division of Regulatory Management and the General Counsel's Office, in which the Medical Officer compiles, organizes, justifies, and correlates the medical and legal facts.

The final task consists of bringing these facts to the United States Attorney who will actually handle the courtroom conduct of the case. Because so many Food and Drug cases vary considerably as to subject material and degree of scientific complexity, the United States Attorney frequently has to be given a rapid briefing in various phases of medicine, in order to be properly equipped and conversant with the subject when he stands alone before the judge and jury. Frequently, if the Medical Officer is an expert in the subject involved, he may take the stand and testify on behalf of the Government.

Miscellaneous problems occupy a good deal of the Medical Officer's time. Much of these are done on time borrowed from other duties and frequently on the doctor's initiative. Cooperative ventures with local health authorities have been most fruitful. Liaison committees have been formed with many national medical organizations. Food and Drug exhibits are shown at medical conventions, and frequently the physician presents a formal paper at the meeting. Another phase of work deals with the preparation of papers explaining the functions of the Food and Drug Administration to the practicing physician. A major function that is a subject of its own is the role of the physician in the New Drug Branch and the Antibiotics Division.

Essentially then, the role of the physician in the Food and Drug Administration is keeping himself aware of medical knowledge and then utilizing this knowledge as it is required under the Food and Drug Act.

The Experimental Pathologist

ROBERT E. ZWICKEY

Pathologist, Pathology Branch
Division of Pharmacology, Food and Drug Administration
Department of Health, Education, and Welfare
Washington, D. C.

The experimental pathologist is a research worker who is trained in the knowledge of gross and microscopic structure and function, and the changes created in these by disease processes. Disease processes such as bacterial, viral, rickettsial, parasitic, dietary, degenerative, neoplastic, and toxic conditions are naturally occurring phenomena having various forms, degrees, and hosts. The experimental pathologist studies artificially induced disease processes under controlled conditions in order to overcome these natural variations. He may be principally concerned with problems involving specific, naturally occurring human or animal diseases, and he may be investigating methods of diagnosis, the pathogenesis, treatment, etiology, and prophylaxis or eradication. In the case of animal disease, he is always concerned with possible threats to the public health. In the Food and Drug Administration and in some commercial laboratories, colleges, and universities, the experimental pathologist is principally concerned with the field of toxicity. In nearly every instance he is one of a team. His colleagues in the fields of pharmacodynamics, biochemistry, pharmacology, hematology, endocrinology, and statistics share the burden of assessing and evaluating the facts that result in conclusions.

The role of the experimental pathologist in the field of toxicology, which is the field dealt with here, is to determine changes in structure and whether the agent administered was responsible. He assigns these findings a place in order of their significance. Often a test substance does not cause the appearance of new types of lesions, but instead increases the incidence and severity of types spontaneously present. When the incidence of naturally occurring disease or changes associated with advancing age in animals receiving a test substance is significantly greater than that present in control animals, the indications are that the test substance is responsible either directly or, probably more often, in various complex and little understood indirect ways. Also, as far as he can, the pathologist tries to equate changes in structure with possible functional changes.

The presence of more or less spontaneous disease in an animal colony (and this will be the case in the older animals of practically every colony) raises the question of whether it would be better to use special "infection free" colonies. Such colonies are not as yet in routine use for toxicity testing, and few data are available with respect to longevity, tumor formation, and old-age degenerative diseases. It would seem that fewer "infection free" animals would be needed to detect significant effects of a toxicant. On the other hand, the human population certainly has its quota of diseases as it approaches its later years. How "infection free" experimental animals ought to be for the results to be of the greatest applicability to man can probably best be settled by actual comparative studies.

An experiment must involve a number of animals sufficient to make possible accurate conclusions. All experimental and control animals should have a careful autopsy done by the pathologist or under his close supervision. In the latter case, deviations from the normal are called to his attention, and he does not miss the opportunity to observe gross alterations. It is not good practice for the experimental pathologist to accept only pieces of tissue sent to him or to limit himself only to histologic examination of sections. While there is need for emphasizing the necessity for careful gross examination or autopsy, this does not detract from the great importance of the histopathologic examination. The most minute deviation in cellular structure is worthy of note. It may not in itself establish any diagnosis, but if its occurrence is repeated, it can be a significant finding. It is, of course, necessary to give proper concern to the histopathologic technique and to identify and separate the inevitable artifacts from changes that are of significance.

A properly planned experiment shows the varying degrees of structural alteration at various dosage levels, ordinarily greatest at the highest dosage levels in chronic experiments and least at one of the lower dosage levels. "Ordinarily" is used because occasionally factors, such as inanition, result in a given dosage level showing greater histologic changes than does a higher dosage level. Because of the varying degree of morphologic evidence of dosage effect, it is necessary to grade the degree and total amount of each change occurring in each animal. Ideally, this will range from none, or a trace, to very slight, and so on up to marked, or even extreme, in occasional instances. Evaluation of histopathologic examination will be greatly facilitated if this information is recorded in tabular form. It is almost impossible to make histologic examinations of a large number of sections from many animals and then mentally to form an accurate clear-cut opinion of the effects of a test substance at the various dosage levels without such a tabular record. It is almost as difficult to read lengthy descriptions of the histologic examination of each organ of many animals and to form a concise and accurate mental summary of the effects.

The effect of the work of the experimental pathologist in the Food and Drug Administration is, together with the other members of the "team" in the fields of pharmacodynamics, biochemistry, pharmacology, hematology, endocrinology, and statistics, to provide a scientific basis and method for determining the safety of a food additive, the risk involved with a drug, or the safety factor of a pesticide residue on agricultural products. Additives to foods so basic in our diet as bread, or additives that may be ingested from several components of our diet, must be as nearly as possible without toxicity. The toxicity of drugs that may be used only infrequently, perhaps as a lifesaving measure, must be viewed in light of the benefit derived as a calculated risk. Pesticide residues on agricultural commodities are an economic necessity today, but they must not be present in such an amount, or be of such a nature, as to eliminate a reasonable safety factor.

The Practicing Physician and the Food
and Drug Administration

HARRY F. DOWLING

Professor of Medicine and Head of the Department
University of Illinois
Chicago, Ill.

Every doctor is familiar with the scene.

The surgeon says, "Number 2 catgut." The instrument nurse, who has already threaded the needle in anticipation of the request, clamps the needle into the needle holder and places the latter in the surgeon's hand. He in turn, without looking at the nurse, waits until he feels the instrument in the palm of his hand and then draws it into the area of his vision. A brief glance serves to verify that it is no. 2 catgut, and without wasting a moment he takes his first stitch.

Although this little drama is repeated every few minutes in countless operating rooms over the world, it is not to its dramatic qualities that I wish to call attention. Its special significance is the surgeon's faith that when he gives the order there will be placed in his hand not only a no. 2 suture properly threaded on a needle that is properly attached to a needle holder, but a sterile no. 2 suture on a needle and a holder that have also been properly sterilized; that no one will have touched the suture or the needle with unsterile hands, nor laid them in an unsterile place, nor even coughed upon them. How can he be so sure of these things? Because he knows that before he has entered the operating room, a team of nurses and attendants, properly trained and supervised and imbued with the knowledge that even the smallest mistake can be fatal for the patient, has taken all the necessary steps beforehand to deliver the no. 2 suture when the surgeon calls for it.

This picture of the surgeon at the operating table illustrates a larger area in which doctors in general take something for granted dozens of times every day. The doctor gives a patient a drug by injection or writes a prescription for it; in so doing he takes for granted that the patient will receive a pure preparation of the drug in exactly the quantity the doctor requested. Furthermore, the doctor takes for granted that this drug will not cause any undue proportion of toxic reactions. How can he be so sure? Because he knows that long before he ordered the drug a team of physicians, chemists, bacteriologists, pharmacologists, and other devoted servants of the health of the public examined the claims of the manufacturers of the drug; studied the reports of numerous physician-investigators; often performed tests themselves; and established and will enforce the standards to which the manufacturers must conform. This group is called the United States Food and Drug Administration. Like the nurses in the operating room, they do their work quietly and with the minimum of bother to the doctor. In fact, so unobtrusive is their work that many doctors do not realize that they exist at all unless some unusual difficulty or some major catastrophe arises.

The work of the Food and Drug Administration touches that of the doctor at many points, however. He may be one of the first to try a new drug, when it is released provisionally for clinical trial. Then the reports that he makes on his cases will be sent to the Food and Drug Administration and will be considered along with others in the determination of the acceptability of, and the standards to be set for, the drug in connection with its release for general distribution.

Second, when the practicing physician learns that a new drug is available for sale he will know that it has passed the rigid tests for safety that have been set up by this Administration. Third, he will be able to ascertain, from the label and from the circular that accompany the drug, the chemical composition, the recommended doses, the indications, and the possible untoward reactions of the drug.

In the advertising of drugs, as in other advertising, statements are frequently made that are equivocal, misleading, or even false. Writers of advertising copy seem to be masters of the art of making an unproved assertion appear obviously true. The busy doctor sometimes feels that he is at the mercy of these people. He seldom has the time to look up the articles upon which the advertiser purports to base his claim. Even if he did, he might find areas of disagreement.* The Food and Drug Administration provides him a solution to this dilemma. The label and the circular that accompany the package must contain full and accurate directions for use that reflect the best informed professional opinion in that field.

Fourth, he can be sure that the drug he prescribes today will be identical in quality, quantity, and purity with the same drug that he prescribed a month ago or a year ago, because the Food and Drug Administration is continually checking on these matters by inspecting the plants of the manufacturers and by testing samples that are purchased from retail pharmacies.

Fifth, if he observes an unusual or suspicious reaction in a patient who has received a certain drug, he can notify the Food and Drug Administration in the sure knowledge that they will find out as quickly and as certainly as they can whether the reaction was due to improper preparation of the drug or to an impurity that has crept in or whether the drug has some hitherto unknown side reaction.

In addition to these services, the Food and Drug Administration is always on the alert to protect the doctor's patients from quacks and other irregular practitioners who use worthless or even harmful drugs or devices to part the patient from his money and his health.

---

* Control of advertising is a function of the Federal Trade Commission.

In certain very vital areas the Food and Drug Administration gives even more help to the doctor and protection to his patients. Insulin and most of the antibiotics must be "certified" before they can be sold. In order for a batch of one of these drugs to be approved for marketing, it must be tested by the laboratories of the Food and Drug Administration as well as by the manufacturer. The drug must be proved to be efficacious and safe, rather than merely safe, as is the case with all the drugs for which certification is not required. The manufacturer is required to keep a record of the distribution of each lot, so that side effects may be searched for and, if necessary, certain lots can be withdrawn from the market. This added protection is given by the Food and Drug Administration at a cost of 0.07 cents added to the average daily dose.

Sixth, if his patient has taken a drug that was not prescribed by a physician, the doctor knows it is one that the great majority of persons can take safely without medical advice. If any of his patients have been deluded by quacks who dispense unauthorized drugs or who use worthless devices, the doctor can call upon the Food and Drug Administration to investigate, and if they find that such decption did take place, to prosecute the offender.

Finally, the Food and Drug Administration also protects the doctor's patients from being deceived with spoiled, filthy, or contaminated food.

This is a brief summary of the ways in which the Food and Drug Administration helps the doctor help his patient. When we consider that all these things are done by a small group of slightly more than 1000 government employees who are protecting the health of some 165 million people, the physician can only echo the famous words of Sir Winston Churchill, "Never did so many owe so much to so few."

III. FOOD AND DRUG ADMINISTRATION AND DRUGS

New Drugs

ERNEST Q. KING

Associate Medical Director, New Drug Branch, Division of Medicine
Food and Drug Administration
U. S. Department of Health, Education, and Welfare
Washington, D. C.

There were no restrictions to the introduction of new, untested, or dangerous drugs into interstate commerce prior to June 25, 1938, and the enactment of the present Food, Drug, and Cosmetic Act. As a consequence, the "Elixir Sulfanilamide Tragedy," which resulted in more than 108 deaths, called to the attention of the country the need for additional legislation to protect the public from similar disasters.

The sulfanilamide tragedy was the result of marketing a diethylene glycol solution of sulfanilamide without investigation of the toxicity of the solvent. Sulfanilamide is not readily soluble in the ordinary safe solvents, and so diethylene glycol was used. Diethylene glycol was subsequently demonstrated to be highly poisonous to all animals tested, so even a simple preliminary animal toxicity test would have precluded its use. With the sudden wave of deaths reported throughout the country, the Food and Drug Administration promptly investigated and arrived at the conclusion that "Elixir Sulfanilamide" was the deadly agent.

Without legal authority to take action on the dangerous drug, the Administration turned its entire inspection force toward the recall and recovery of the drug before more people were killed. This was done on the basis that elixir sulfanilamide was misbranded, inasmuch as it was not an "elixir," that is an alcoholic solution, but a diethylene glycol solution.

New Food and Drug legislation had been introduced in numerous sessions of Congress, but failed to pass. However, with the "Elixir Sulfanilamide" tragedy as a spearhead, the Federal Food, Drug, and Cosmetic Act of 1938 was enacted with provisions that all "new drugs" must be shown to be safe for use prior to marketing.

The term "new drug" was, by this law, given a legal definition, and an application was required. In the application, full details of the investigations conducted to evaluate the drug's safety, its components, the method of manufacture, and controls were required. Responsibility fell on the Food and Drug Administration to evaluate all applications and determine whether they were complete, whether adequate study had been conducted to evaluate the safety of the preparations, and whether the articles could be safely used.

Some of the pharmaceutical industry felt that progress would be stifled, since it was well recognized that practically any potent drug had dangerous potentialities. However, the Food and Drug Administration has always weighed the therapeutic value of the drug against its toxicity and has given particular attention to safeguards, such as informative labeling to warn physicians against potential dangers. As a result, pharmacologic and clinical research have become important fields in many of the leading medical institutions.

The results are reflected through the most startling advancements in medicine. New drugs, which have been evaluated by the Food and Drug Administration, now account for more than 90 per cent of all the prescriptions written today. Many dreaded diseases are now readily treated. Pneumonia is no longer the "captain of death." Syphilis is rapidly and effectively treated by penicillin. Treatment of tuberculosis has been simplified through streptomycin, isoniazid, and p-aminosalicylic acid. A few micrograms of vitamin B_{12} can reverse the development of pernicious anemia. Adrenocorticotropic hormone, cortisone, and other corticosteroids may be lifesaving and aid in the rehabilitation of many. Progress has been made in the treatment of hypertension, mental disease, and malignant disease. Pharmacology, which formerly was considered a minor subject in many medical schools, is now recognized as among the most important.

More than 10,000 new drug applications have been reviewed by the Food and Drug Administration. Working under a strict time limitation of 60 to 180 days and under severe handicaps of insufficient staff, the New Drug Branch of the Food and Drug Administration has accomplished an outstanding service in the field of public health.

The Pharmacologist Investigates a Drug

A. J. LEHMAN

Chief, Division of Pharmacology, Food and Drug Administration
Department of Health, Education, and Welfare
Washington, D. C.

"People are rather unpredictable and don't always die when they are supposed to, and don't always recover when they should. All in all, we must depend heavily on laboratory experimentation for sound and controllable basic principles." This statement made recently by Dr. Arthur L. Tatum, Emeritus Professor of Pharmacology, University of Wisconsin, is comprehensive in expressing the importance of laboratory evidence in establishing the safety and usefulness of a new drug. The experimental approach for developing the data may vary somewhat depending on the objectives, but considering this from the aspect of the clinician only, the more important experimental phases that should be undertaken include acute and chronic toxicity, pharmacodynamics, and pathology.

Acute Toxicity. This, usually the beginning phase of the experimental studies, has for its purpose the determination of the effect of the drug under investigation when administered as a single dose or as multiple doses over a period of 24 hours or less. Two terms are commonly used to express the end results: ED_{50} and LD_{50}. They represent the amount of the drug usually expressed in milligrams or grams per kilogram of body weight that is required to effect a response (ED_{50}) or be fatal (LD_{50}) to approximately one half of a group of animals of a certain species under specified conditions. These values are important in estimating "margins of safety," but even more significant is the character of the response. If the ED_{50} and LD_{50} as determined in several species of animals are all of the same order of magnitude, it is a safe assumption that man will respond similarly to a comparable dose. If considerable variation exists among the animal species, the difficulties in estimating the probable two dosage values for man are greatly increased. When confronted with data of this type in support of a new drug application, it has always been our position to regard man as at least as sensitive as the most sensitive species of animals tested.

Pharmacodynamics. The second step in the evaluation program should logically proceed to a study of the mechanism and site of action of the drug. The investigation should emphasize the organ or system that is influenced by the drug. Much useful information will be obtained from these studies for appraising the ultimate benefits that may derive from the new therapeutic agent. An understanding of its pharmacodynamics provides for the planning of dosage schedules and routes of administration. The nature of the side effects is usually demonstrated, and often specific antidotes can be recommended in cases of overdosage. Clues to contraindications and possible irrational or harmful combinations of drugs may be revealed, and the pathologist is frequently alerted where to look with special care for histopathologic changes.

Prolonged Administration. The two previous phases emphasized the effects a single or, at the most, a few doses of the drug may produce. Adequate therapy may require multiple doses and for extended periods of time. For a drug that is administered for an occasional acute illness, observation in animals should be from one to three months' duration. In chronic diseases, which require more prolonged use of a drug, the animal observations should be extended to six months or to a year. The methods of administration should follow human usage, and dosage schedules should include a low dose of the same order of magnitude as the human dose, and a high dose sufficient to produce definite toxicology or histopathology. A rodent and nonrodent species is advisable in each study. Because of the trend toward maintenance dosage of drugs, perhaps even for the lifetime of an individual, it is becoming increasingly apparent that long-term studies in animals to include lifetime exposure of at least one species, notably the rat, may be necessary for certain such drugs.

Special Observations. Additional studies, whenever they apply, include reactions or irritation at the site of injection, the biochemical behavior of the drug with respect to blood and tissue levels, storage of the drug in tissues and whether stored as the parent compound or as a metabolite, stability of the storage depot, and the significance of the relative proportions of the metabolite and parent compound should both be present. Biologic control procedures should also be included to insure a finished drug free from harmful impurities, such as pyrogens, bacteria, accidental contaminants, and undesirable decomposition products.

Pathology. Practical considerations dictate the type and thoroughness of the pathologic studies that should be done on the test animals. In many instances, in fact, the pathologist has the final word in the evaluation of the hazards and usefulness of a drug. It has been our experience that much valuable information is sometimes lost by the practice of sending small fixed portions of the various organs to the pathologist after a relatively untrained person has performed a perfunctory autopsy. Submitting lesions only for examination without an adequate amount of adjacent tissue is likewise not satisfactory. In the Food and Drug Administration laboratories, it is the practice to employ the "find out" approach, a detailed tabulation of all observations, because our experience has been that this is the only procedure suitable for detecting the more subtle tissue changes.

Finally, when the investigations of the pharmacologist and the associated studies of the biochemist, physiologist, and pathologist have been assembled and interpreted, recommendations can be made with respect to man.

Side Effects of Drugs

E. C. HAGAN

Pharmacologist, Acute Toxicity Branch
Division of Pharmacology, Food and Drug Administration
Department of Health, Education, and Welfare
Washington, D. C.

Alexander, in his book entitled *Reactions with Drug Therapy*, has defined drug hypersensitivity as that which "connotes mechanisms that are responsible for lesions which differ from pharmacological effects of those of overdosage, and which are induced by therapeutic or subtherapeutic amounts." In addition, there are equally ardent advocates of the theory that such sensitivity is dependent on the size of dosage, that response increases uniformly with the dose. Many instances of so-called sensitivity can be explained on this basis.

However, we would like to indulge in an expansion of the term "side effects of drugs" to include not only those reactions that may result from hypersensitivity, the latter said to be due to an allergic mechanism, but also to those effects that may simply result from an inadequate testing program. Such reactions may, therefore, include those expected from a toxic level of the drug. Animal toxicity studies can be designed to protect both the normally susceptible and the hypersensitive groups. This is accomplished for the normally sensitive group by requiring that there be an adequate margin of safety, and for the hypersensitive groups by appropriate tests for allergic manifestations by administration of the drug to animals peculiarly suited to such tests.

Margin of safety may be defined as the ratio of the therapeutic dose of a drug to the level that will just cause untoward effects. If this ratio is sufficiently high, the hazards of administering that drug to the public will be greatly diminished.

Testing procedures for the determination of the adequacy of drugs from a safety standpoint include not only the aforementioned toxicity studies, but also a standardization of the potency of the drug by chemical or biologic means, as well as rigid tests to insure proper hydrogen ion concentration, and sterility, where such tests are pertinent.

To go back a number of years, this complaint of inadequate testing, which has been long-standing, was brought into sharper focus by the unfortunate deaths that occurred as a result of the use of the "elixir sulfanilimide" in drug therapy. The responsible toxic agent contained in the drug preparation was the solvent, diethylene glycol. This incident occurred in 1937, and further pointed up the need for the "New Drug" provisions contained in the Food, Drug, and Cosmetic Act, which was passed one year later. Under these provisions, before a new drug can be distributed in interstate commerce, evidence of the safety of the article for the purposes intended must be submitted to the Food and Drug Administration in the form of a new drug application. However, despite the scope of the drug act, there remain instances in which more thorough testing of a drug or a druglike product would have prevented unfortunate incidents. In particular, reference is made to the salt substitute episode in which lithium chloride was offered for sale as a replacement for sodium chloride in those individuals who, as a result of heart conditions, could not tolerate the retention of fluids induced by diets of normal sodium chloride content. As a result of reports of toxic effects in persons using this product, lithium chloride was fed to laboratory animals. Deaths occurred at levels that did not provide a sufficient margin of safety. Further, the toxicity was accentuated when lithium was given to animals maintained on diets greatly restricted as to their sodium chloride content. Suffice it to say that the adverse effects noted in people using this product might have been prevented had a more adequate testing program been conducted.

The following are additional examples of complaints of injury that have led to the implication of various drug products. The drugs found to be at fault were (1) a local anesthetic solution with excessive hydrogen ion concentration which resulted in death of tissues at the site of injection; (2) a veterinary salt solution which caused untoward effects and deaths in animals to which it was given intravenously. These effects resulted from failure of the label to bear adequate warnings that the drug should not be given too rapidly. A simple animal test would have prevented this. (3) Drugs for injection containing injurious quantities of surface active agents. These resulted in local damage at the injection sites. Many more such situations can be enumerated, but these suffice to impress one with the necessity not only for full investigations of a drug before it is put on the market, but also for careful control procedures as long as its production is continued.

Finally, an important consideration in the therapeutic field is that of synergism of drugs where only simple additive effects are anticipated. Often drugs, which of themselves are wholly satisfactory, will, when combined, eventuate in an extremely dangerous drug combination. It is for this reason that new combinations of old drugs are also required to have their safety established in a new drug application before they are marketed.

Inert Glandular Preparations

ERNEST J. UMBERGER

Pharmacologist, Endocrine Branch, Division of Pharmacology
Food and Drug Administration
Department of Health, Education, and Welfare
Washington, D. C.

How one aspect of the enforcement philosophy of food and drug law has kept pace with the development of a rapidly growing scientific field is shown by the Food and Drug Administration's attitude toward inert glandular preparations.

Coincident with the turn of the century and the passage of the original Federal Food and Drugs Act of 1906, there occurred one of the most important advances in medical science. This was the discovery and the recognition that certain organs within the body synthesized materials (hormones) that regulated the function of distant parts of the same organism. When disease occurred due to the failure of one of these organs or glands to synthesize its hormone, it was found experimentally that the condition could be corrected by treatment with an appropriately prepared extract of the corresponding functional gland of domestic animals. Examples are the successful treatment of myxedema and cretinism with thyroid, and the successful treatment of diabetes with insulin extracted from the pancreas. These medical successes stimulated the empiric use of extracts from many other glands and organs of animal bodies.

Much painstaking research was performed toward the isolation and identification of the active principles of the glands. As a result of this research, it was discovered that in most cases the producing gland does not store any appreciable amount of the hormone it manufactures. As a consequence, the experts in this field recognize that many of the commercial glandular preparations sold as drugs were essentially inert and worthless for the treatment of disease, since they did not contain a significant amount of the hormone supposedly present. The Food and Drug Administration therefore embarked on a program designed to discourage the distribution of these inert glandular preparations for drug use.

The administrative consideration of the status of these inert glandular preparations went through several phases. One of the widely promoted glandular materials was that of the ovary, marketed in dry, powdered form or as an extract of the gland. When scientific evidence became available that these ovarian gland preparations were devoid of physiologic activity, the Food and Drug Administration announced in 1939 through trade correspondence that no statement should appear on the label of such an article implying that physiologically or therapeutically active ingredients were present. In 1940, the Administration went further and expressed the view that persons distributing inert ovarian preparations should state positively in the labeling of such an article that there was no scientific evidence that such ovarian preparations possessed any therapeutic activity. This view was further broadened in 1941 when the Administration notified the drug trade that the labeling of any inert glandular material should include a forthright and conspicuously displayed statement to the effect that the article does not contain any known therapeutically useful constituent of the gland or glands mentioned in the labeling of the article.

As more information accumulated to the effect that a number of glandular preparations on the market were devoid of any glandular activity, it became apparent that the steps taken previously by the Administration had not been sufficient for preventing the marketing of worthless drug preparations in violation of the Federal Food, Drug, and Cosmetic Act of 1938. Therefore, in March 1948, the Administration inserted in the *Federal Register* a "notice to manufacturers, packers, and distributors of glandular preparations." After defining the term "inert glandular materials" as meaning preparations "incapable of exerting an action or effect of some significant or measurable benefit in one way or another" when used as a medicinal agent, the notice pointed out that it is obviously impossible to write adequate directions for the use of a preparation that is inert. Therefore, under the terms of the Federal Food, Drug, and Cosmetic Act, it was not possible to prepare a legal labeling for such "inert glandular materials," and consequently "such articles will be considered to be misbranded if they are distributed for use as drugs."

The *Federal Register* notice of March 1948 has been followed up by a program of regulatory action designed to remove "inert glandular materials" from the channels of drug trade.

In short, the Administration's handling of the "inert glandular materials" problem was based on the parallel development of accurate scientific knowledge concerning the nature of the active principles of glandular extracts. The scientific finding that many commercial glandular preparations were devoid of any effectiveness for medicinal use resulted in regulatory action against them.

The Pharmacologist Looks at Cancer Chemotherapeutic Agents

GEOFFREY WOODARD

Chief, Pharmacodynamics Branch, Division of Pharmacology
Food and Drug Administration
Department of Health, Education, and Welfare
Washington, D. C.

Within the past 10 years, cancer chemotherapy has advanced from a not quite respectable field to one that is held today as one of the most promising areas in the control of cancer. Ten or 15 years ago, responsible public health officials looked askance at products alleged to be effective in the treatment of cancer. Today, the weight of scientific evidence is still overwhelming against the effectiveness of the so-called "cancer cures" employed by "fringe" practitioners. However, with the advent of the use of nitrogen mustards in the treatment of neoplastic diseases, we have seen the development of several series of compounds having utility in cancer chemotherapy. These include several compounds of the "mustard-like" or alkylating type, folic acid antagonists, purine antagonists, and hormone type compounds. Unlike the nostrums of the past, these are potent, highly active substances. They affect many systems in the body rather seriously. Their effectiveness lies in their selective toxicity for the rapidly growing and dividing tumor cells. Herein is the work for the pharmacologist. He must determine qualitatively, as well as quantitatively, the nature and extent of this selective toxicity.

The Food and Drug Administration, through the new drug application procedure has a great responsibility in the field of cancer chemotherapy. In permitting a new drug application to become effective for a cancer chemotherapeutic drug, a careful balance between the utility in the treatment of a very serious neoplastic disease on the one hand, and the toxicity to the patient on the other, must be reached. A large part of the necessary evidence can be obtained by the pharmacologist. He not only determines the usual laboratory animal toxicities but also contributes to the knowledge concerning the mechanisms of action of the drug, effective blood or tissue levels, and the pathways of absorption, distribution, and excretion. Inasmuch as the drugs so far developed for cancer chemotherapy are quite toxic, the aid that the pharmacologist can give in planning the most efficient clinical dosage schedule may mean the difference between success and failure.

Through an implemented working agreement between the Cancer Chemotherapy Service Center of the National Cancer Institute and the Food and Drug Administration, the pharmacologic work-up of a number of potential cancer chemotherapeutic drugs is under way. In addition to supplying necessary data preliminary to clinical trial, this program also is giving pharmacologists in the Food and Drug Administration practical experience in, and an understanding of, the problems involved in gathering evidence for safety of drugs in cancer chemotherapy.

Beyond the practical problems involved in obtaining pharmacologic and toxicologic data on new compounds, there is a challenge to pharmacologists working in fundamental fields. For example, the development of drug resistance is quite common. Drug resistance is a fundamental pharmacologic problem. Differential behavior between normal and tumor cells in response to known drugs is virtually an unexplored field. There may be differences in the permeability of cell membranes, in the number of drug receptor sites per cell, or in the internal organization of the cell that may be exploited by the pharmacologist in the development of a drug with suitable selective toxicity for tumor cells. Pharmacologists working in these or related areas may well provide the clue necessary for the chemical control of cancer. The development of an adequate chemical control of cancer obviously will put the nostrum purveyor and "cancer quack" out of business.

The Importance of the Bioassay of Digitalis

HERBERT A. BRAUN

Chief, Cardiac Branch
Division of Pharmacology, Food and Drug Administration
Department of Health, Education, and Welfare
Washington, D. C.

Digitalis is a potent, therapeutically active drug that is dangerous when administered in excessive amounts. Crude digitalis leaves may vary greatly in potency and therapeutic efficacy. Some samples of this drug are almost inert, while other samples may be from two to five times more potent physiologically.

The desire of the practitioner to obtain digitalis preparations of constant strength is as old as digitalis therapy. In his book, *An Account of the Foxglove*, which Withering published in 1785, he gave exact directions for the collection and storage of the crude drug and for the preparation of its various galenicals. As a further check, he observed the physiologic effects of digitalis on his patients during treatment. In spite of Withering's recommendations, the fulfillment of his desire for a preparation of uniform activity was still in the far distant future, but the danger of the effects of the drug had been lessened due to the precautions that were recommended by him.

Digitalis is one of the most important drugs used in medicine for which the most recent chemical and physical methods in use in our laboratories do not as yet yield satisfactory results for its standardization. It is true that within the last few years various digitalis glycosides have been isolated and are now being produced commercially. With the isolation of the chemically pure, crystalline glycosides from the crude drug, crystalline standards can now be used for the chemical standardization of the pure glycosides. As the result of this, the U.S.P. XV monographs contain chemical and physical constants for some of these glycosides, as well as chemical standardizations. However, so far no chemical determination that measures the therapeutic action of the total glycosides and their genins in the crude digitalis leaf or of its preparations has been developed.

The physician who prescribes digitalis is not particularly interested in the absolute potency of a digitalis preparation. He is, however, concerned that the potency of a preparation is so adjusted that it will give him the same clinical response as is produced by any other brand of digitalis purchased on the open market. It is therefore essential, in order to be certain of a uniform therapeutic response to the same dose of digitalis, that this drug be standardized biologically.

Biologic standardizations or bioassays are determinations of potency by which the strength of the active principles of a drug is measured on the intact living animal or on a surviving organ.

The first bioassay of digitalis was developed in Cushny's laboratory by Houghton in 1898. He used the systolic standstill of the frog's heart as an end point. The U.S.P. IX, which became official in 1916, adopted an optional one hour frog method in its monograph on digitalis. The next revision of the U.S.P., namely, the U.S.P. X, contained mandatory bioassays for digitalis, strophanthus, and squill. In the U.S.P. XII the one hour frog method was replaced by the intravenous cat method. The reason for supplanting the frog method by the cat method is that digitalis preparations that have been aged showed deterioration with the frog assay but retained their original strength when assayed on cats and humans. In this revision also, for the first time, a U.S.P. digitalis reference powder was adopted as a standard of reference. It was equal in potency to the international standard powder. Soon after the adoption of the intravenous cat method, it became apparent that cats were difficult to obtain and were too expensive. The U.S.P. XIV then substituted an intravenous pigeon method for the intravenous cat method after first determining that there was close agreement of the pigeon method with the cat and human assays. The intravenous pigeon method has been retained in the U.S.P. XV.

In European and South American countries, the frog, cat, and guinea pig methods are used extensively for assaying digitalis. All of these methods are based on the permanent stoppage of the test animal's heart.

It has frequently been argued that there is no relationship between the use of permanent standstill of an animal's heart as an end point in an assay and the therapeutic efficacy of a preparation of digitalis on the heart of a human being, since digitalis is used as a cardiac tonic in the case of man and not to stop the heart of an animal. This argument, of course, is fallacious, since the effectiveness of the cat and pigeon methods for the bioassay of digitalis is based on results obtained by the standardization of digitalis on humans.

The Food and Drug Administration enforces the standards included in the text of the *United States Pharmacopeia*. Despite the fact that pure glycosides of digitalis have been prescribed extensively in recent years according to the latest issue of the Red Book, there are more than 50 pharmaceutical manufacturers and repackagers in this country who are marketing digitalis preparations. Due to a lack of funds and available personnel, the Division of Pharmacology of the Food and Drug Administration is unable to assay every batch of digitalis preparation manufactured in the United States. However, a survey of the preparations on the market is made, and adulteration of the preparations is detected by means of biologic assay of digitalis preparations. This is another of the many ways in which the Food and Drug Administration seeks to protect both the physician and his patient.

Standardization of Hypotensive Drugs

L. M. LUSKY

Pharmacologist, Cardiac Branch
Division of Pharmacology, Food and Drug Administration
Department of Health, Education, and Welfare
Washington, D. C.

One function of the Food and Drug Administration is to protect the public from possible harm from new drugs. In recent years an incredible number of drugs have been developed and proposed for the relief of hypertension. Most of these are potentially dangerous and many depend on precise dosage for their therapeutic efficiency. Some are manufactured in chemically pure form and can be made to conform to specific chemical standards. There are, however, several hypotensive drugs that are devoid of characteristic chemical or physical properties that would serve for their identification and assay. The determination of their potency depends on their reaction with living matter.

Progress in the field of biologic standardization followed recognition of the inadequacy of attempts to define the potency of a drug in animal units, based on observation of individual reactions produced in animals. It is now generally acknowledged that all such units are variable. They vary because of the difference in individual response of any given group of test animals, because of the variation in the mean response of colonies of animals in different laboratories, and because of the differences in detail of techniques of the pharmacologists.

All modern methods of biologic standardization are fundamentally comparative. The introduction of standards in the form of stable preparations makes these comparative methods possible, for every assay of the potency of an unknown becomes a comparison with the potency of a standard. The importance of these standards cannot be overemphasized, for they are the basis of official drug standardization.

The establishment of reference standards marked a turning point in other developments of biologic standardization, since the increased precision that was now possible encouraged the introduction of biometric concepts in designing methods and analyzing data.

When a new drug is developed, there usually is a period between its introduction and its inclusion in the *United States Pharmacopeia*. During this period, the drug obviously cannot be officially standardized. In this interval, it is necessary to determine whether the manufacturer can achieve the production of a uniform product. If the product is one requiring bioassay, the manufacturer can determine its uniformity by comparing each new lot of the drug with a single lot set aside as a "reference substance" or a "house standard."

The uniformity and potency of many of the drugs used in the management of hypertension, such as hexamethonium, hydralazine, thiocynate, and nitroprusside, can be determined by physical and chemical means. The physical and chemical tests usually can be completed in a short time, and the accuracy of such methods is usually greater than that obtained by biologic means. These drugs therefore do not create a great problem relating to manufacturers' control.

There appear to be as many methods of standardization of a new drug as there are pharmacologists developing them. Biologic standardization, especially in the preliminary stage, is applied scientific research. The pharmacologists, like most scientists, are individualists and are seldom willing to copy each other's techniques in detail, and so their methods vary from one to the other. Nevertheless, there are basic principles and techniques that are commonly used in drug standardization. Methods may be considered good if they are accurate, rapid, and simple; and poor if they are inaccurate, slow, and require unusual skill in technique. Claude Bernard, the great French physiologist, once said: "In biological sciences, the role of method is even more important than in other sciences because of the complexity of phenomena and the countless source of error."

In recent years, there have been numerous assays proposed for the biologic standardization of the alkaloids of veratrum. Test animals proposed for use in these assays include frogs, mice, cats, dogs, and guinea pigs. The end points are various physiologic responses ranging from a drop in blood pressure to toxic symptoms or deaths in the test group. It has often been demonstrated that if two preparations of a substance are compared in different laboratories, the ratio of potency of the two is usually found to be the same, although one laboratory may use a different test animal and a different physiologic response as an end point. This is true only in properly designed and developed assays in which details of technique have been well worked out. At present, at least two methods are used in the assay of veratrum: the blood pressure method in the dog and the mouse toxicity method.

Rauwolfia serpentina is a drug recently introduced in this country for the control of hypertension and for use in other branches of medicine. The root of *R. serpentina* is a complex mixture of substances. Alkaloids comprise 0.5 to 1.5 per cent of its weight. The chemical characteristics of the crude drug are incomplete and often contradictory; the existence of some of its alkaloids has been challenged. Of the alkaloids, reserpine has received most attention, and the experimental results with this alkaloid are in relatively good agreement. Because of widespread use of these drugs, the Food and Drug Administration has focused special attention on their production. At present, personnel of three scientific divisions of the Administration are actively engaged in the development of methods of identification and standardization.

The manufacturers' control of drugs that are potentially as dangerous as these hypotensive agents must be complete and accurate. The nature of these substances makes it necessary at times to use the bioassay to insure uniformity of potency. Many methods of bioassay are very accurate and reproducible; others require a large number of animals to reduce the standard error. In the course of their development, data are collected, the evaluation of which gives additional information relating to the mode of action, side reactions and toxicity, accumulation, specie variation, and therapeutic dose schedules.

In the United States, the drug products that the physician receives from the manufacturer are standardized to a uniform potency and are the end result of thorough and exacting scientific investigations.

Pyrogens in Parenteral Preparations

WILLIAM D. HARKNESS

Pharmacologist, Pharmacodynamics Branch
Division of Pharmacology, Food and Drug Administration
Department of Health, Education, and Welfare
Washington, D. C.

The occurrence of fever in patients who had received injections of sterile solutions was observed many years ago. As early as 1911, the German literature contained references to such undesired reactions following the injection of arsphenamine in the treatment of syphilis. For some years, no comprehensive studies were reported in this field; then about 1923 Seibert and co-workers at Yale University conducted exhaustive experiments in various animals and confirmed the fact that these reactions were traceable to bacteria that had at some time existed in the injectable solutions, or particularly in the water used in their preparation. Viability, or even the presence of dead organisms, was found to be unnecessary for the appearance of this pyrogenic effect in humans. In fact, sterilization by methods that are today acceptable in that they effectively eliminate bacteria in the solutions is of no value in removing the so-called pyrogens once the bacteria have remained in the solution for even a brief period of growth.

During the next 15 years or so, a growing number of studies were reported that increased the general knowledge in the field of pyrogens. The importance of maintaining freedom from pyrogens in parenteral preparations, particularly those that are used in large volume, such as normal saline or dextrose solutions, was finally given official recognition when a pyrogen test using rabbits as the test animal was included in the U.S.P. XII following extensive collaborative work by the Food and Drug Administration, the National Institutes of Health, and several commercial laboratories. This test, with only slight modifications, is still the accepted official method in use today. Basically, it is a simple safety test in which the rabbits are injected intravenously, and any effect on their body temperature is observed and evaluated. With the increased knowledge about the factors responsible for pyrogenicity and the use of the adequate test method, tremendous improvement has been shown by the entire industry. In recent years, only rarely have pyrogenic large-volume parenteral preparations been encountered on the market.

With the publication of the U.S.P. XV, which became effective on December 15, 1955, another forward stride has been made with respect to the question of pyrogens. Freedom from pyrogens, at that time, became a requirement for a number of additional preparations that are injected only in relatively small volume. Experience has shown that some of the small-volume injectable preparations can become contaminated to the extent that they produce undesired temperature rises in patients.

As the testing of the additional drugs for pyrogens becomes a routine procedure, the chances of a contaminated product reaching the market are greatly lowered. Actually, as all conscientious manufacturers of injectable preparations know, the possibility of pyrogens occurring in injectable solutions is practically nonexistent if accepted procedures of handling, filling, and sterilization within short enough time limits are rigidly followed. In other words, the presence or absence of pyrogens in the finished product is a pretty good index of the kind of "housekeeping" practiced. The Food and Drug Administration maintains a continuing surveillance of the various injectable drugs for pyrogen contamination.

We will make a few generalizations regarding the future of the pyrogen problem. First, there may be a few additional products not now covered by pyrogen requirements in the pharmacopeia which should have that requirement. Some investigative work is necessary to reveal what these products are and to determine the dosage level and other factors necessary before pyrogen testing could be required. New injectable solutions still to appear on the market present a similar problem. That is, at the time of investigating the actions and effects of the product before its introduction, the desirability and feasibility of a pyrogen test should be ascertained. Finally, we might mention that there is still much to be learned with respect to the exact nature of pyrogens chemically. Studies along this line have indicated that some pyrogens have a high molecular polysaccharide structure. It is possible that conclusive evidence of the exact chemical identity of various pyrogenic substances will lead to even better methods for their detection, control, and elimination.

Claims for Vitamins

E. M. NELSON AND O. L. KLINE

Division of Nutrition
Food and Drug Administration
Department of Health, Education, and Welfare
Washington, D. C.

Claims of benefit from the use of vitamins for all ills continue to increase, with no sign of a plateau in sight. Scientific information developed during the last decade has given us a basis for understanding the needs for the vitamins in human nutrition, and something of their physiologic functions, and it is important to point out the educational need for a common sense point of view toward this problem.

Vitamins must be considered as nutrients, along with the other constituents of food, i.e., carbohydrate, fat, protein, salts, and water. A complete lack of any one of these substances causes dire changes in the metabolism of the experimental animal. This metabolism is normal when adequate amounts of these constituents are consumed, and excesses, within limits, are neither harmful nor beneficial.

Human requirements for the vitamins are set forth in the form of Recommended Dietary Allowances published by the Food and Nutrition Board of the National Research Council. These figures are for the amounts of each of the vitamins that must be present in the diet to meet the needs of a wide variety of individuals. It is not difficult to meet these requirements with the goods available in the grocery store. In fact, it is fair to assert that for the most part the American population does obtain its vitamin requirements in this way.

There are instances, of course, where vitamin products are prescribed and used with good reason. In this country the age of outright vitamin deficiency disease in the adult, seen during the depression days of the 1930's, is past, and the well-informed physician must look closely to determine whether or not symptoms and signs observed indicate faulty nutrition.

Even so, the less than scrupulous purveyor of vitamin products continues blatantly to call attention, in every possible medium, to the likelihood that "that tired feeling," stress of many kinds, or being run-down indicate subclinical deficiency and the need for vitamin supplementation of the diet. The nature of claims made to promote the sale of an article has undergone a gradual change, since the Food and Drug Administration has been successful in court against openly misleading claims. It is no longer a common practice to say "Our product is guaranteed to cure all skin diseases or your money back." Such a statement is too easy to disprove. Now the purveyor of such an article uses clever qualifications that lead to double talk, or he may even go so far as to state the specific conditions under which a product will not be effective, with the implication that under conditions other than those specified, it is effective. Scare technique of emphasizing dangers to health are still common weapons, not confined to the printed page, but used also by door-to-door salesmen and health food lecturers.

Vitamin deficiency, the artful copywriter states, is the result of depleted soils that produce foods of inferior nutritive value. This has been refuted by sound scientific evidence except for the case of iodine. He implies great losses of vitamins in food processing, transportation, storage, and cooking. Bear in mind that in home cooking before the last generation there was little knowledge of how to prevent these losses. But in the modern processing of food, it is in the best interest of the manufacturer to know of and to prevent such losses and to provide a food of highest possible nutritive value. Better methods of home cooking also are in wide use. Highly questionable are the claims of benefit for so-called unidentified nutritional factors said to be present in a few milligrams of a concentrate prepared from natural plant sources. If such factors exist, how much more likely it is that they will be obtained by consuming the natural foods themselves. Claims for great value of high potency therapeutic vitamin dosage are presented with such force and volume that the patient, we are told, now demands of the doctor treatment with vitamins he has heard and seen described.

Various kinds of stress are said to increase the need for vitamin supplementation, with every change in our environment and every change in food or water intake subjecting the living body to a stress that must be overcome by the intake of extra vitamins. Why? We hunt in vain for some evidence to support this vague theory. In a recently stated concept of stress by Dr. Selye, it has been defined as a nonspecific deviation from the normal resting state caused by function or damage, which stimulates repair. The endocrine and nervous systems are most important in this response, and it is suggested that the adrenal cortex and the anterior pituitary are the great co-ordinators. In efforts to increase the sale of vitamin products, this concept is extended to imply an increased nutritional requirement in stress. We can find without difficulty data that tell us this application is not valid.

44

In fact, the theory would just as well permit the conclusion that an excessive intake of vitamins would produce stress.

The stress of infection has been a particular focal point in vitamin claims. It is proposed that vitamins are an aid in the prevention or treatment of infection. That there is no established value of vitamins in this relationship was well stated in the summary of a recent symposium on nutrition in infections: "That the papers presented here are a heterogeneous lot is, I think, almost an historical necessity, for it is now more obvious than ever that there is no clear and simple connection between infection and nutrition that has won universal assent." In the same vein, Goldsmith has concluded that the influence of vitamin nutrition on resistance to specific infections in the human subject remains largely unknown. Further, the paucity of information relative to the efficacy of antibiotic-vitamin combinations precludes any attempt to evaluate this method of therapy at the present time. She states finally that there is no magic formula that can relieve the practicing clinician from the detailed analysis of all facets of the patient's nutritive state.

The daily diet, if taken in sufficient amounts to supply the needed energy and protein, under most conditions will supply the vitamins necessary to utilize that energy and protein. There are conditions that the physician, with care will recognize, which require a supplemental intake of vitamins, either for nutritional or psychologic reasons, but this does not imply or support the claim that deficiency disease is widespread. Vitamin products, used intelligently and with some degree of common sense and understanding, have a definite place in medicine.

Self-styled nutritionists, on the other hand, should not be treating disease or persuading the public to use "health foods" for conditions requiring rational medical care. The Food and Drug Administration has been able to take court actions when a definite association can be established between false claims (either oral or written) and a specific product. The situation can be met only by public education, however, when the propaganda is spread by books, magazine articles, general lectures, and other means beyond the reaches of the Federal law.

Measurement of Vitamin Potency

CHESTER D. TOLLE AND O. L. KLINE
Department of Health, Education, and Welfare
Food and Drug Administration
Division of Nutrition
Washington, D. C.

In the first decade of this century this country was at peace with the world, and most food chemists were satisfied that classified methods of analysis for nitrogen, fiber, soluble carbohydrate, and ash content of foods yielded all the information necessary to assess the nutritive value of our food supply. However, during the second and third decades, it was discovered that foods contain additional nutritive qualities and that vitamins, present in extremely small amounts in foods, are essential for life. With knowledge of their importance, methods of measuring their presence were soon developed. A new science of nutrition has grown up, based largely on the knowledge of vitamin content of foods, and the physiologic function of these factors in the growth and metabolism of man and animals. Progress in the development of this information has been dependent upon the ingenuity of the chemist in devising new and novel means of measuring the presence of complex and sometimes unstable substances found in quantities expressed, not in terms of ounces, or per cents, but as parts per million, or as micrograms, a millionth part of a gram.

For the most part, discovery of vitamins was made by observing physiologic changes in animals maintained on artificial or purified diets that were so constituted as to be devoid of one of the essential nutrients. For example, rats or chicks fed a ration heated under specific conditions were observed to develop a syndrome called polyneuritis. When it was learned that this was the result of a deficiency of thiamine, destroyed in the ration by the heat process, the deficient animal served as a means of detecting the presence of thiamine in any test substance added to the diet. Under strictly controlled conditions, such a measurement was made quantitative, with an acceptable degree of precision.

For a number of years the U.S.P. method for determining thiamine was one involving the cure of polyneuritis in rats under carefully controlled conditions. Today vitamin D is the only vitamin for which the official method involves the use of animals.

Measurement of vitamins in animals by biologic assay methods is difficult, time-consuming, and costly. Chemists were encouraged to find more rapid means of detecting these complex substances, not only in foods, but in tissues of animals to guide the search for the way the vitamins function in the animal body.

In the 1930's, when a number of the vitamins were isolated, crystallized, and synthesized, more was learned of their chemical properties, some of which could be used as a basis for measurement. For example, it was learned that fluorescence is a property that is useful in detecting quantitatively minute quantities of riboflavin in a solution of known volume. Thiamine was found to undergo a chemical reaction upon oxidation in alkaline solution to form a new compound called thiochrome, highly fluorescent in ultraviolet light. This property of fluorescence is the basis for quantitative measurement of both thiamine and riboflavin, by chemical methods that have been adopted by chemists throughout the world. The U. S. Pharmacopoeia contains descriptions of these methods. In wide use also are chemical methods for niacin and folic acid, based upon development of color that can be measured in a suitable photometer.

Vitamins, like all other compounds, have the property of absorbing light at specific wavelengths. Vitamin A, for example, has a maximum absorption of light at a wavelength of 328 millimicrons. If a vitamin capsule or tablet containing vitamin A is saponified by treatment with alkali in alcoholic solution, then extracted in petroleum ether, and finally further purified by selective adsorption and elution on a column of alumina (chromatography), the final solution containing vitamin A may be examined in a spectrophotometer, and the vitamin A estimated from the amount of light absorption at an appropriate wavelength. This is now a commonly used accurate technique for those substances that are sufficiently pure, or that can be purified without difficulty.

Another important analytical tool used to measure vitamin potency is called analytical microbiology. This involves the use of a microorganism, a *Lactobacillus*, for example, that is induced to grow in a purified medium, to which are added small, graded amounts of the vitamin under study. We know that the bacterium *Lactobacillus arabinosus* cannot grow if its culture medium is devoid of pantothenic acid. When a small fraction of a microgram of this vitamin is added to a test tube containing the medium, the organism will grow and produce acid that can be measured by titration with alkali. Or, if the analyst wishes, the amount of growth, and therefore the amount of vitamin, is determined by measuring the increase in the turbidity of the liquid. This kind of approach has been most useful, not only for vitamin determinations, but for estimation of amino acids, as well as for identifying many of the intermediary compounds produced by animal metabolism.

Present-day procedures for control of the vitamin content of pharmaceutical products and enriched foods are rapid and precise. While the bioassay requires weeks for a result, most of our vitamin methods are now completed in a few hours. From careful studies of reproducibility of methods, and of the differences in results from one laboratory to another, control chemists have learned to measure vitamin potency to within a few per cent of the true value.

Pharmaceutical and food industry laboratories are well equipped to make certain that the products they produce contain within narrow limits the vitamin content indicated on the label.

In the regulatory program of the Food and Drug Administration, the methods used for the examination of the vitamin content of products in interstate commerce are those described in the U. S. Pharmacopoeia and in the AOAC Book of Methods. These procedures have been established as reliable and acceptable by collaborative study in a number of laboratories. In maintaining a sound and effective regulatory program it is important to have analyses of this kind conducted by chemists who have been trained to use these complex methods. A high degree of precision is important in assuring the physician and the patient that the products of commerce are of labeled potency.

In the Food and Drug Administration's laboratories there is a continuing program of study to improve these methods and also to develop new ones. This has paid dividends in the saving of time by utilizing shorter procedures, and in improved precision. Such improvements continue to increase the coverage that can be given to products bearing nutritional claims that are subject to the Food, Drug, and Cosmetic Act. More rapid analyses make it possible to remove from commerce before they are distributed to the consumer those products that are seriously adulterated. There is more to be done. With the appearance of new claims for nutritional value, and for unusual benefits that appeal to the consumer, new methods of testing must be devised.

Enzymes in Drug and Food Technology

HERBERT BLUMENTHAL

Pharmacologist, Acute Toxicity Branch
Division of Pharmacology, Food and Drug Administration
Department of Health, Education, and Welfare
Washington, D. C.

Fermentation in its broadest sense may be defined as the decomposition of complex molecules through microbial action. As such, it is one of man's oldest technologic processes. However, it was only after Pasteur, in 1871, demonstrated the role of microorganisms in wine making that fermentations were taken out of the realm of spontaneous phenomena. With the advent of aseptic techniques and controlled inocula, a new era in fermentation technology began. The discovery and characterization of new organisms resulted in a concomitant increase in favorable products. Today, fermentative processes are utilized in the manufacture of a large number of basic organic compounds, which include such substances as ethanol, glycerol, butanol, acetone, 2,3-butylene glycol, citric acid, lactic acid, gluconic acid, acetic acid, and sorbose. In addition, fermentative processes are employed in the production of a number of the B vitamins and most of the antibiotics.

With the recognition of enzymes as specific entities, procedures based on the use of individual enzymes or enzyme complexes rather than whole organisms have been introduced. Thus, in the food industry there are a number of important processes based on the use of enzyme preparations.

Of the enzyme preparations used commercially, diastase probably has the largest application. The greatest commercial use for diastase is the conversion of starch to fermentable sugars in fermentation industries. Malt is used in this work, and it provides both the starch and the enzyme source. The production of syrups via the hydrolysis of starch is another use for diastase. The baking industry is also a larger user of diastase where it serves to even the texture of certain baked goods. A specialized diastase preparation active at a low pH that will attack starch and not pectin is used to clear pectin so that jellies will not appear clouded.

Other saccharolytic enzymes in use are invertase, which converts sucrose to invert sugar, thus increasing sweetness and reducing the tendency to crystallize, and lactase, used to hydrolyze lactose, thus reducing its tendency to crystallize out in products high in milk solids.

A second class of enzymes used in the food industries are the proteinases. Chill proofing of beer is a proteinase application designed to prevent haze in beer upon chilling. Such haze is due to the presence of proteins and can be prevented by partial hydrolysis, which results in their increased solubility. This hydrolysis, however, must not be so complete as to destroy the foaming properties in the beer. Proteinases, such as papain, are also used in tenderizing meat, and rennin has long been used to clot milk in certain dairy processes.

Lipolytic enzymes have no wide application in food processing, although the use of lipase in some cheese-ripening processes appears promising.

Pectinases are used in the clarification of fruit juices and in the processing of fruit concentrates.

The use of enzyme preparations by the pharmaceutical industry has become more prevalent in recent years. For a long time, the only enzymes used as therapeutic aids were pepsin and rennin as digestive aids, and diastase for digestive disturbances or in the preliminary treatment of starches for baby foods. A number of years ago, the Germans introduced the use of proteolytic enzymes as a means of clearing away necrotic and scarred tissues. Today there are a number of proteolytic enzyme preparations available for this and similar purposes.

Streptokinase-streptodornase is a preparation of bacterial origin active at neutral pH. Its history goes back to the 1900's when it was noted that blood contained fibrinolytic material. It was later found that streptococci capable of producing rapidly spreading infections elaborated a material capable of causing the lysis of clots. Ultimately it was shown that the fibrinolytic activity of such streptococci was due to streptokinase, an activator for human fibrinolysin present in plasma. The streptococci were also shown to elaborate a number of true lytic enzymes, among which is streptodornase, which depolymerizes desoxyribose nucleic acids. Streptokinase-streptodornase preparations are well-suited for clot digestion but are limited by the fact that the concentration of fibrinolysin in plasma varies. In wounds that are highly acid or alkaline, buffers at neutral pH must be used.

Crystalline trypsin, obtained from bovine pancreas, is a proteolytic enzyme active at neutral or slightly alkaline pH. It is more active than fibrinolysin. However, its activity is also more short-lived, since it rapidly digests itself. It has the advantage of yielding a standard activity per unit weight and can attack necrotic tissues and proteins other than fibrin. Plasma normally contains a trypsin inhibitor, the concentration of which increases with injury and reaches a maximum in about 10 days, so that increasing doses must be used.

Proteolytic enzymes have also been used in the preparation of protein hydrolysates as nutritional supplements or intravenous preparations. Pancreatic extract preparations are in use for patients with pancreatic insufficiency or chronic gastric enteritis. Hyaluronidase, an enzyme that hydrolyses hyaluronic acid, a polysaccharide that is the chief constituent in cellular cement, has been used as an aid in infiltrative local anesthesia, hypodermoclysis, and similar situations.

For the future, it is conceivable that as their value in practical applications is realized more enzymes will be taken out of the laboratory and put to practical use, and as knowledge increases we will reach a stage where enzymes will be custom built to meet specific needs. Steps in this direction are already in evidence. The classic work of Sanger's group in England, in elucidating the actual structure of the insulin molecule, has opened the way for the analysis of protein structure. Already the structure of some of the posterior pituitary hormones have been or are being worked out.

The job of synthesizing large protein molecules is, of course, a long way off. If one were to consider the average protein molecule, the number of possible isomers would be formidable. However, the problem may not be this complex. Recent evidence suggests that for many enzymes the active sites are relatively small, and the peptides on the order of 50 amino acid residues have all the activity of the parent molecules. Thus, the future of the increased use of enzymes as therapeutic aids appears extremely promising. Where such applications result in a product going directly to the consumer, the Food and Drug Administration will be concerned. New products mean new standards, not only of purity but also of potency, and potency in enzymes means critical measurement of a specific activity. Problems such as antigenicity for injectable preparations, loss of potency due to route of administration, and side effects, as well as whether the product does what the label claims, will be explored. The varied experience of the Food and Drug Administration should assure that these problems will be met and dealt with as they appear.

The Role of the Food and Drug Administration in the Control of the Salk Vaccine

ARTHUR A. CHECCHI
Division of Field Operations
Food and Drug Administration
Department of Health, Education, and Welfare
Washington, D. C.

Events in the spring and early summer of 1955 emphasized the fact that the public interest required some sort of program to provide for a dependable flow of safe and efficacious poliomyelitis vaccine to the American consumer. Because of the tremendous and inherent popular demand for such a vaccine, it appeared that at least in the early stages there would not be sufficient quantities available to supply immunization treatments to all who might desire them. Recognizing that these early shortages created an atmosphere conducive to illegal operations, the Congress, through a special appropriation for the fiscal year July 1, 1955, to June 30, 1956, commissioned the Food and Drug Administration to take the necessary steps within the framework of the Federal Food, Drug, and Cosmetic Act to insure that the vaccine remained in legal drug commerce. To the Public Health Service fell the task of devising and instituting adequate tests for the safety and efficacy of the vaccine, the decision as to which batches could be released for use, and the responsibility for establishing an equitable distribution program.

The Food and Drug Administration concluded that it could best fulfill its obligations under this program by soliciting and utilizing the full cooperation of the drug industry. Arrangements were made with the manufacturers of the vaccine to furnish to the Food and Drug Administration complete records of distribution on each batch of vaccine released by the Public Health Service. This information is relayed to each of the 16 field Districts of the Food and Drug Administration in whose territories the consignees are located. Taking particular care to give equitable coverage by manufacturers, geographic areas, and population concentrations, representative shipments are selected for investigation to make certain that the vaccine reaches the intended consignees and in the invoiced quantity. This often involved visiting two or more persons to track down one shipment.

Hundreds of such visits to drug distributors, retail pharmacies, physicians, hospitals, health agencies, and private homes are made each week by Food and Drug Administration inspectors. The cases of improper handling of the vaccine found to date have not been such as to warrant any conclusions as to the existence of black marketeering or other illegal operations. Instances of possible use outside of the authorized age groups and other violations of the voluntary distribution program, but not of the Federal Food, Drug, and Cosmetic Act, are referred to the Public Health Service for possible referral to the appropriate professional societies for voluntary correction.

While they have not been numerous, reports of black market operations have appeared in the public press. The most alarming one was in a "sensational" pocket-type magazine that alleged that more than one third of the vaccine produced was being diverted to black market operations and that physicians were charging from $40 to $80 for immunization treatments. These reports and those received from other sources have been promptly investigated by the Food and Drug Administration but thus far have been found to be without foundation.

While the primary purpose of the Food and Drug Administration's participation in the program is to guard against illegal distribution of the vaccine, there is ample evidence that its inspectors have made other valuable contributions in the interest of the consumers and the medical profession. For example, whenever in the course of their work they find instances in which the vaccine has been held beyond the labeled expiration date or stored without proper refrigeration—thereby creating potential health hazards—the facts are immediately made known to the persons involved and also called to the attention of the Public Health Service. Such experiences have created an increasing awareness on the part of the receivers and handlers of the vaccine to store it under proper refrigeration, to make sure that it is used before the expiration date, or that such outdated material should be withheld from use pending suitable disposition.

While there have been a few occasions of misunderstanding on the part of physicians and druggists of the role being played by the Government in the poliomyelitis vaccine distribution program, they welcome this effort to make certain that vaccine received through legitimate channels can be administered to patients with the confidence that is so necessary to the practice of medicine. The Food and Drug Administration hopes that the fact that its inspectors make routine visits to physicians and pharmacists has served to stimulate this confidence.

The How and Why of the Certification of Insulin

R. L. GRANT
Chief, Insulin Branch
Division of Pharmacology, Food and Drug Administration
Department of Health, Education, and Welfare
Washington, D. C.

When the Food, Drug, and Cosmetic Act was amended in December, 1941, to require that insulin-containing drugs be certified by the Food and Drug Administration, it was the intent of Congress to assure for all diabetics safe, effective drugs by continuing a special type of control that had been maintained over insulin. It is fortunate that Banting and his associates saw the need and used the rights granted them by patents to license manufacturers and to maintain control over the insulin produced. This control was exercised by the Insulin Committee of the University of Toronto, which established a testing laboratory for checking the strength, quality, and purity of the insulin produced by its licensees. This laboratory assayed for potency every new lot of insulin produced in the United States as a check on the result obtained by the manufacturer and then required that samples of every batch (dilution ready for sale to the user) be submitted for testing.

Shortly before the expiration date of one of the important patents under which the Insulin Committee maintained control of insulin drugs, the need for continuing this predistribution testing became a subject of concern to the American Medical Association, the Board of Trustees of the *United States Pharmacopoeia*, and others interested in the welfare of users of insulin. The House of Representatives' Committee on Interstate and Foreign Commerce in recommending the amendment to the Food, Drug, and Cosmetic Act providing for the certification of insulin-containing drugs stated the reasons for this concern:

"The life expectancy of users of insulin would be short if the drug were not available. With it, most of these sufferers can live a normal span. Each user of insulin must learn through his physician the quantity and frequency of dosage necessary for him. Most diabetics subsequently buy insulin direct from drug stores and administer it to themselves with only occasional check ups by physicians. If the drug is too strong, insulin convulsions may follow and even death. If it is too weak, coma may result from which the patient may not recover. Such results are particularly likely if he is relying upon himself alone for the administration of the drug. With no other drug are the consequences of failure of accurate standardization so dramatic and so immediate."

The inadequacy of the usual regulatory control by the Food and Drug Administration, which permits examination of samples of drugs only after they have been distributed in interstate commerce, was pointed out in the same report:

"Even when a sample is collected promptly after the shipment reaches its destination considerable time for distribution occurs because the assay is time-consuming; the gravity of consequences which might ensue from the distribution of improperly standardized products before the sanctions of the law could be invoked can easily be imagined."

Congress acted promptly, and, within three days after the bill had been introduced, it was passed by both the House and the Senate. Three days later on December 22, 1941, just one day before the patent expired, it was signed by the President and became a law. The Food, Drug, and Cosmetic Act was thereby amended to require that drugs containing insulin be certified and that regulations be promulgated providing for their certification.

The regulations were drafted in collaboration with the insulin manufacturers and with the advice of the Insulin Committee. They provide for a continuation of the two-assay control to establish the potency of each new lot of insulin and for the examination by the Food and Drug Administration of each batch of finished drug before it can be distributed. Not only must the insulin used to make the batch be approved, but also, if the batch contains a modifying agent, such as protamine or globin, that must be approved, as well as the trial mixture made from the particular lots of the modifying agent and the insulin intended for use in making batches of the drug. The two most important steps in the certification procedure are the approval of the insulin that establishes the potency and the approval of the trial mixture that establishes the pattern for future batches. The examination of the finished batch then requires testing for sterility and determinations of pH, nitrogen, and zinc to assure us that it is a safe and effective drug.

The insulin regulations have been amended from time to time to provide for better test methods, to drop unnecessary requirements, and to provide for the certification of new insulin-containing drugs that have an effective new drug application. The original regulations provided for the certification of batches of insulin and protamine zinc insulin; subsequent amendments provided for the certification of globin zinc insulin, NPH insulin, and lente insulin.

Certification of Antibiotics

DONALD C. GROVE
Department of Health, Education, and Welfare
Food and Drug Administration
Washington, D. C.

A little more than 10 years ago on July 6, 1945, Congress amended the Federal Food, Drug, and Cosmetic Act to require the certification of each batch of penicillin and its derivatives before shipment in commerce. In 1947 the Act was further amended to include certification of streptomycin and again in 1949 for chlortetracycline, bacitracin, and chloramphenicol and their derivatives. Since this last amendment, there has been some controversy concerning the need for certification of these drugs. It is believed of interest therefore to review this decade of special Government control of these drugs and to consider the future status of such a program.

From July 6, 1945, to January 1, 1955, 271 companies used the certification services and 136,389 batches, totaling approximately 3246 tons of penicillin, streptomycin, dihydrostreptomycin, chlortetracycline, tetracycline, chloramphenicol, and bacitracin, have been examined by the Food and Drug Administration. It is estimated that this quantity of antibiotics represents 7.8 billion usual daily doses. Of the batches examined, 635 or approximately 8.7 tons failed to comply with the standards. In addition, 370 batches, representing 13.9 tons, failed to meet the standards but the request for certification was withdrawn by the company involved before rejection. The total rejected or withdrawn batches, 1005, amount to 22.5 tons or approximately 70 million daily doses. The total cost of the certification service during this period of time, which is entirely borne by industry, was approximately 5.7 million dollars.

The primary purpose of certification of each batch of these antibiotics by the Government before commercial distribution by the manufacturer is to afford greater protection to the health of the consumer. Such benefit is accomplished by:

1. Double testing. Each manufacturer is required to test the batch and it is again tested by the Food and Drug Administration.

2. Factory inspection prior to certification. Firms must have adequate manufacturing facilities or certification is refused.

3. Proof of both safety and efficacy for new certifiable antibiotic products. This prevents distribution of worthless products that might be nontoxic but therapeutically ineffective. Other new drugs under the Act require proof of safety only.

4. Requiring records of distribution. Manufacturers have to keep distribution records of each batch and, if for any reason a batch should have to be recalled from the market, this can be accomplished very promptly. This is not required for other drugs with the exception of insulin.

5. Prior approval of labeling. All labeling, including proper dosage, indications, contraindications, and directions for use, must be approved prior to marketing.

6. Power to stop distribution completely. In the event of an emergency where something serious might develop, refusal to certify would stop distribution.

While the merits of the certification procedure in the protection of the public health are recognized by the manufacturers, many feel that adequate protection can be obtained without certification. This belief is based mainly upon their own record of satisfactorily producing other important drugs without double checking or certification by the Government. While this is true, one should keep in mind that those other drugs cover a much narrower range of therapeutic usefulness and affect a much smaller segment of the public than the antibiotics. Prescription surveys have shown that 40 per cent of the dollar volume of all prescriptions is for antibiotic preparations.

Another argument advanced against certification is that several antibiotics have been developed since the last certification amendment to the Act and have been satisfactorily distributed under the regular provisions of the Act without certification, the most important of these being oxytetracycline and erythromycin. So far this has been true, but perhaps the reason for this success lies in the limited number of manufacturers. Thus, oxytetracycline is controlled by only one firm and erythromycin by only three, all four of which use the certification services for other antibiotics.

Some companies have objected to the cost of certification, which must be paid for by industry. In this respect it is not believed that the cost is excessive. The average cost for certification of a batch is about $42.00. This may vary from $12.00 to $150.00, depending upon the size of the batch and the tests to be made. It has been calculated that during the 10 years of certification the average cost per usual daily dose was 0.07 cent.

Some point to the low average percentage of lots (approximately 0.7 per cent) rejected or withdrawn for failure to meet the standards during this 10 year period as a further reason for no longer needing certification. However, one would expect this figure to be low, since manufacturers generally do not submit lots that have not passed their own tests. In other words, batches submitted for certification are hand picked. Also, while the rejection rate was low, it still represented 70 million substandard daily doses that were prevented from reaching the consumer.

A study of antibiotic certification, along with the other Food and Drug Administration functions, was made by the Citizens Advisory Committee appointed by the Secretary of Health, Education, and Welfare, and in its report of June, 1955, the following conclusions were reached:

"1. *****, the Committee feels that the appropriate authorities should consider taking such steps as are administratively permissible under the present Act to decertify antibiotics which have reached standards of identity, strength, quality, and purity which are sufficiently satisfactory to warrant decertification.

"2. The Committee also feels that it would be desirable for the FDA to establish technical criteria for the administrative exemption of antibiotics and antibiotic dosage forms and that these criteria be made known officially to producers of antibiotics for their guidance and for maximum protection of the public.

"3. With the decertification of some antibiotics, the loss of income to the FDA would require additional appropriated funds to assure adequate testing and control of antibiotics subject to certification, as well as the testing on a sampling basis of decertified antibiotics to assure that standards are maintained."

The antibiotic drugs used in the treatment of so many serious diseases and affecting the public health of such a vast portion of our population are certainly too important suddenly to stop certification of all of them at once. The conclusions reached by the Citizens Committee are logical ones and would permit decertification after satisfactory criteria have been developed to establish their safe release. After their decertification, the Committee has wisely recommended that appropriations be provided for market sampling to insure compliance with the established standards.

The Food and Drug Administration has had discussions in the past with members of industry regarding the criteria that should be established for decertification of an antibiotic. These discussions have raised such questions as: How many batches of a product should a firm have certified before the firm would be released from the necessity for certification of this product? How long a period of time should a firm have to be under the certification requirements before release could be considered? How many rejections during such time period or number of batches should be allowed, or should there be zero rejections? Should release be granted to each individual manufacturer based on his own record, or should decertification of a product be granted to all manufacturers simultaneously?

These are a few of the questions raised and they are difficult to answer. However, progress has been made and it is believed a set of criteria acceptable to both industry and the Food and Drug Administration can be worked out. When this is done, a gradual and orderly decertification of antibiotics can then begin without danger to the public health.

A Pharmaceutical Manufacturer Looks at the Food and Drug Administration

ROBERT A. HARDT

*Vice President, Hoffmann-La Roche Inc., Nutley, N. J., and
Member of the Citizens Advisory Committee for
the Food and Drug Administration*

June 30, 1956, will mark the Fiftieth Anniversary of our national Pure Food, Drug, and Cosmetic Act, which was first enacted in 1906 as the Federal Food and Drugs Act. The pharmaceutical industry is participating enthusiastically in the commemoration of this anniversary.

When I was a student in college, my professor of pharmacognosy, the late Dr. Albert Schneider, frequently referred in his lectures to a law that he called the Wiley Act. He held this act in high esteem, as he did the man who fought so long and so diligently for its enactment, the late Dr. Harvey W. Wiley. Of course, Dr. Schneider was referring to the Food and Drugs Act of 1906, which was the predecessor of our present law enacted in 1938.

The 1906 law was a good law for its time. It was, however, essentially a policing act designed to protect the public against fraudulent practices and to safeguard the integrity of drugs. It could not serve as a guide or a direction finder for the more specific and dramatic progress in drug therapy that we have been privileged to witness in our time.

Sometimes the laws that govern men and institutions serve to strengthen rather than suppress. Sometimes they do this with mutual benefit to all concerned. Sometimes, but not always, they do this with only temporary inconvenience and relatively light burdens of compliance. Sometimes, if intelligently and properly enforced and administered, a law can be good for everyone. This, I think, can properly be said of the Federal Food, Drug, and Cosmetic Act.

The enactment of this statute unquestionably gave impetus to drug therapy and to the growth of the pharmaceutical industry. Certainly, the miracle climb of the industry coincides reasonably well with the period during which the Act has been in force. The provisions of the Act have necessitated and even encouraged collection of vastly increased data about medicinal products used in the diagnosis, prevention, and treatment of disease.

This increase in information collected about drugs and their uses taught us several things: (1) We learned that there probably is no perfect drug. If a drug is potent and effective, certain side effects in some patients are to be expected. Such knowledge about a specific drug need not necessarily condemn it but could call for more care and watchfulness in its use, for example, in modified-dosage systems and improved administration techniques. (2) As we collected more information required for filing new-drug applications, our researches led us to modifications and new compounds that were even more useful in treating certain diseases. We learned more about acute- and chronic-toxicity tests. All in all, there has been a really significant advance in clinical research activities in the pharmaceutical industry. For example, one clinical study about which I have personal knowledge embraced the study of the effect of a drug on the blood of more than 5000 patients. Included in this large group of patients under study were some who previously exhibited sensitivity or toxicity to related compounds. (3) We learned to distinguish in a much more sharply definitive way between objective and subjective data—that is, we developed methods by which we could determine what was actually happening to patients and what seemed to be happening.

Research in the pharmaceutical industry has assisted materially in the progress of medicine. Today the average life span has risen to 69 years. Among primitive people, the average span was less than 20 years. Then, in the expanding knowledge of the great civilization of Greece, it remained for Hippocrates to set medicine on a realistic and rational course. In his time the average span of life rose to 37 years. In Victorian days, man could look forward to only 47 years of life. But today, because of the advance of science and because of better medicine, the span of life has risen to 69 years. We of the pharmaceutical industry do not flatter ourselves that this advance has been due entirely to our efforts. We do not claim, nor do we want, more than our share of the credit.

In the latter part of October, 1955, the pharmaceutical industry had the privilege of presenting itself to social studies teachers of the nation at The Industrial Council Session on the Pharmaceutical Industry at Rensselaer Polytechnic Institute. At this symposium, social studies teachers from all states of the Union had the opportunity to ask questions of leaders in the pharmaceutical industry.

A question frequently asked was: What is the relationship of industry to the Food and Drug Administration? The answer to this question was given by both industry leaders and Food and Drug Administration officials. In essence the answer was that the relationship is one of friendly and constructive cooperation between the Food and Drug Administration and the better element of the industry.

This statement should not be construed as suggesting that there is always perfect agreement between the industry and the FDA. That is certainly not the case. However, much can be accomplished when reasonable men sit down together to discuss problems affecting the public welfare.

Thus far, at least, the administrators of the law have been dedicated and devoted people who have enforced it courageously, equitably, and in the public interest.

The flow of new pharmaceuticals imposes a greater public health responsibility than ever before on the drug-distribution system of our country. I should therefore call attention to the danger inherent in excessive administrative power. The Food and Drug Law is full of mysteries. The Food and Drug Administration seeks to resolve these mysteries through administrative regulations and interpretations.

We of the pharmaceutical industry recognize the difficulties which beset that agency. Likewise, we appreciate and understand its deep interest in public health. Nevertheless, our attention is not diverted from the overriding principle that the functions and authority of the agency are determined by legislation which represents what the Congress considers as best suited to protect the public health.

Experience has taught the need for vigilance. There is always the danger that regulations will impair the traditional concepts of the practice of medicine. Progress in the treatment or prevention of disease should not be hampered or unnecessarily delayed by those who seek power only for the sake of power.

Administrative policies are most productive when they conform to legislative authority. The current administrators of the Food and Drug Administration have demonstrated in many ways that they are aware of this fact.

The leaders of the pharmaceutical industry have a very deep sense of their responsibility to the public just as do most of our legislators. They are willing to accept this responsibility as a matter of honor with a minimum of regulation.

Nevertheless, the Food and Drug Law has and will continue to be a strong force in the progress of our industry. That is why I am pleased to have had the privilege of briefly relating to physicians some of the story of the pharmaceutical industry's relationship to the FDA.

The Skin Game

J. H. DRAIZE
Chief, Skin Toxicity Branch
Division of Pharmacology, Food and Drug Administration
Department of Health, Education, and Welfare
Washington, D. C.

Modern chemistry and technology are responsible for a rapidly expanding group of synthetic products. Many such new synthetic products have been proposed for use or are actually used in cosmetics and topical medicines. In our modern industrial world, not only the plant worker engaged in the manufacturing and handling of these synthetic chemicals, but also to a lesser extent, the average individual regardless of occupation may be exposed to a wide variety of new chemical substances that have been introduced in his daily living. The need has arisen for the proper appraisal of the health hazards involved in the cutaneous and mucous membrane exposure to these products. Adequate appraisal of such hazards poses many problems in skin pharmacology and toxicology.

The Division of Pharmacology of the Food and Drug Administration is often called upon to review dermal and mucous membrane toxicity data, and to pass on the adequacy of such data, in support of evidence to demonstrate safety for use of a product. In addition, the division frequently finds it necessary to obtain its own toxicity data to permit decisions on products which may be in violation of the provisions of the Federal Food, Drug, and Cosmetic Act.

The skin is a large and important organ of the body. No other organ is exposed to as many or as varied external (often detrimental) influences, namely, wide fluctuations in external temperatures and humidity, and such other physical factors as chemical irritants, bacteria, virus agents, and any other offending material that may be present in man's environment. An important physiologic function of the skin is its role in serving as protective armor for the deeper tissues against trauma and desiccation. In addition, the intact skin also serves as a relatively effective barrier to the inward transfer or penetration of many substances. Paradoxically, the skin has been found permeable in some degree to a wide variety of substances. This is significant not only in cosmetics and topical medicine, but also, from toxicologic implications, in forensic medicine.

Although the skin must be regarded as an entity comprising the epidermis, derma, and subcutis, problems in absorption are confined chiefly to considerations of the epidermal layers. Substances that have reached the derma with its extreme vascularity, readily enter the general circulation. The epidermis with its many imperfections or "breaks" in its architecture (as represented by the skin appendages: the sebaceous and sweat glands and their ducts, and the hair follicles) presents a sievelike structure capable of engulfing considerable material which in a physiologic sense has neither penetrated nor been absorbed. It is characteristic of warm-blooded animals that the outer cell layers of skin desquamate constantly and uninterruptedly. This gradual desquamation of outer cells of the horny layer illustrates a primary function of mammalian skin, namely, a characteristic designed to prevent the inward movement of materials that may come in contact with the skin. The process of cornification in the epidermis, that is, the formation of keratins, which are refractory chemical substances, is further evidence that the epidermis is a tough inert barrier to the percutaneous inward transfer of materials. Mammalian skin in its physical and physiologic behavior illustrates the principle that a most important function of this organ is to exclude, slough, and expel materials rather than to abet their penetration and absorption.

For obvious reasons, man is not the feasible experimental subject to use in the acquisition of the bulk of the data in the determination of dermal or mucous membrane toxicity. Reliance for the evaluation of the toxicity of substances must be placed on laboratory animals.

Procedures to evaluate the toxicity of substances applied topically to skin and mucous membranes are numerous and involved. The various techniques are designed to estimate local effects (local toxicity) as well as systemic effects (systemic toxicity). The local effects are more properly termed "irritations," a general term to describe essentially contact dermatoses or inflammation of mucous membranes. Skin irritation may result from contact with substances that are primary irritants or from contact with substances producing sensitizations. A third type of skin irritation is now recognized which, for the lack of a better term, has been named "skin fatigue." Appraisal of systemic toxicity is made following dermal applications by acute (single) and subacute (multiple) exposures to the test substance. Exposures are made to the intact as well as the damaged skin. Data should include observations on symptomology, chemical studies, hematology, pathology, and physiologic function tests on treated subjects. Great significance is attached to a careful histopathologic examination of tissues of animals following treatment in the longer periods of multiple exposures.

It is not uncommon in studying compounds by the various dermal techniques to observe in some instances but slight effects on acute (single) exposure. However, the same compound may be found severely damaging when studied by subacute (multiple) exposures. The skin damage may range from a mild dermatitis to complete necrosis or severe eschar formation with desquamation. In such instances, the regenerating skin, as a rule, is more resistant to future action of the compound.

Adequate methods are available today to study the local and systemic toxicity of substances applied topically to skin and mucous membranes, and to permit an appraisal or evaluation of the extent of injury produced in these structures. Such procedures yield information on prognosis for repair and recovery. Analysis and assessment of data, a consideration of species differences, and the allowance for a margin of safety make possible an estimation, in the case of a given compound, of the amounts, concentration, and frequency of application that may be tolerated by man.

Dermal Sensitization

FRANCIS X. WAZETER

Pharmacologist, Skin Toxicity Branch
Division of Pharmacology, Food and Drug Administration
Washington, D. C.

Several forms of allergic manifestations are known and distinctly recognizable. They are categorized as (1) anaphylactic, (2) bacterial or tuberculin, and (3) dermal, cutaneous, or eczematous sensitizations. The third category is of particular interest to the Skin Toxicity Branch of the Food and Drug Administration.

Problems involving dermal sensitization have become of paramount importance, particularly within recent years, owing to the increased use of synthetic agents for cosmetic and detergent purposes. Irritation of the skin following the topical application of a cosmetic, or contact with a detergent, can occur in one of two forms. The response could be one of primary irritation, and if so, the causative agent is referred to as a primary irritant. While its mechanism of action is not fully understood, it is related, at least in part, to the inherent nature of the substance, its concentration, and the duration of exposure. In such cases, skin eruption is confined to the site of contact or application of the offending agent. In contrast to this, the skin can be exposed one or more times to a particular compound without the occurrence of an untoward response. However, with repeated or frequent exposure, as would result from the use of a cosmetic or detergent, a skin reaction may be elicited although the concentration of the compound is low and the exposure time short. Such a phenomenon is thought of as having been acquired, or the individual sensitized, and the condition is diagnosed as eczematous or contact dermatitis. Should the skin react in similar fashion following frequent short periods of exposure to a known primary irritant present in low concentration, the irritant is considered to be also a sensitizer.

Since Landsteiner's demonstration, some 20 years ago, that guinea pig skin can be sensitized to various compounds, skin sensitization has been studied extensively. The guinea pig has continued to be the animal of choice in such experimental procedures. Landsteiner's intracutaneous method, subsequently modified by Draize, has been employed with a fair degree of success in the food, drug, and cosmetic work carried out by the testing and research units of the Food and Drug Administration. It has been our experience that substances which sensitize the guinea pig are invariably capable of causing a similar effect in man. The weakness of the method lies in the fact that some substances, classed as nonsensitizers on the basis of this test, are later found to cause sensitization in man. Its greatest value would seem to be as a screening test to eliminate most of the sensitizers prior to human experimentation. A theoretic disadvantage of the method is the route of sensitization, since most compounds eliciting eczematous dermatitis do so as a result of repeated or continuous contact with the skin.

The Schwartz prophetic patch test is still widely used in screening compounds as potential sensitizers and employs human beings as the experimental subject. The method consists of a single exposure applied as a patch and remaining in contact with the skin for 48 hours to five days, followed by a single challenge patch 10 to 14 days later. This test is considered inadequate because only the most powerful sensitizers are capable of producing a response following a single exposure.

The Food and Drug Administration is of the opinion that a more suitable method of procedure is needed to determine the sensitizing power of new agents. At present, the Skin Toxicity Branch, in addition to its routine investigation and evaluation of new products, is conducting a full-time research program in the hope of either developing a new procedure for measuring sensitizing abilities of compounds, or improving one of the methods currently employed. While any new test must, of necessity, be designed for the evaluation of compounds that might sensitize man, such a method should employ an experimental tool other than the human being. If animals are used, the test should be of such nature that compounds capable of sensitizing the animal evoke a similar response in man. The converse also must hold. Finally, exposure to the compound should include topical application rather than other routes of sensitization since most cases of eczematous dermatitis are of the contact type.

A Cosmetic Manufacturer Looks at the Food and Drug Administration

RICHARD SALOMON
President, Charles of the Ritz
New York, N. Y.

Some cosmetic manufacturers recall vividly their original reactions to news they received in 1938 that henceforward their activities would come under the scrutiny of the Food and Drug Administration.

At that time the cosmetic field had to some extent surrendered its claim to public belief in its advertising and labeling. Many of us recall well a flood of turtle oil creams and other concoctions that promised complete miracles of rejuvenation, and contained no turtle oil and performed no miracles. Nevertheless, most manufacturers agreed that the advent of additional Government controls was most unwelcome, and they have foretold in gloomy terms our approaching doom. Many believed that we would be hamstrung by unintelligent and unsympathetic handling of cosmetic controls by the Food and Drug Administration.

Be it said to the credit of the industry as a whole, responsible manufacturers determined to do all in their power to win the confidence of the Food and Drug Administration, and at the same time the confidence of the buying public. In its turn the FDA took an intelligent approach to the industry, sympathized with the problems we faced, and in many instances suggested methods by which we could overcome our difficulties. In no case, to my knowledge, was a purely arbitrary or bureaucratic stand taken.

As a result over a period of several years, the industry and the Administration came to understand each other. The unsound business practices of some manufacturers were abandoned, and the general buying public learned more and more to trust the advertising and labeling claims of the manufacturers of toilet preparations. Far from the doom that was foretold at the time, the industry prospered and grew. To some degree, this growth is a reflection of increasing public confidence in us and in our products, and very possibly a reliance on the fact that cosmetics are known to be under good supervisory control.

Another effect upon the industry was a stimulation to creative research, which has characterized to a greater or lesser degree all of the responsible companies in our field. We have made great technical advances in our products, and up to now have not suffered undue restraint from the intelligent officials we have had to deal with at the Food and Drug Administration. That science was to play an increasingly important part in our field was recognized by the industry. At the May 1936 Convention of the Toilet Goods Association, the members unanimously voted to form a Board of Standards to study and advise the industry on questions of a scientific nature, as well as labeling and advertising claims. A few years later, the Scientific Section of this Association was formed. Scientific papers presented at May and December meetings are published in the Proceedings of the Scientific Section, which is the first American technical journal devoted exclusively to the cosmetic field. A professional scientific society in our field has been formed; namely, The Society of Cosmetic Chemists. This Society has branches in England and other countries. The Journal of the Society of Cosmetic Chemists is esteemed and respected throughout the world. Scientists of the Food and Drug Administration have presented 15 papers before the Scientific Section of the Toilet Goods Association. These excellent studies made in their Washington laboratories have been of great help in guiding the progress of our industry with special reference to safety and efficacy.

All of these moves on the part of a responsible industry, whose products are vital to the consumer, have been fostered in the atmosphere engendered by Congress' decision to place the manufacturing of our products and their packaging under the auspices of the Food and Drug Administration.

In facing the future it is my belief that most manufacturers are pleased with the progress to date and with the attitude of the Administration. We believe that it would be helpful if the budget of FDA were to be increased so as to provide funds for some basic research, which most of the companies in our field are incapable of undertaking either individually or collectively. Such research on the effects of raw materials on the human body would be most helpful and greatly welcomed by an industry that is today determined to work as closely as possible with the FDA.

IV. FOOD AND DRUG ADMINISTRATION AND FOODS

Food and Drug Law and Nutrition

E. M. NELSON

Chief, Division of Nutrition, Food and Drug Administration
Department of Health, Education, and Welfare
Washington, D. C.

The year 1956 marks the fiftieth year of enforcement in this country of Federal legislation pertaining to foods and drugs, a milestone that invites reflection upon the relation of such legislation to problems of nutrition. Our knowledge of nutrition has developed, to a large degree, since the passage of the Food and Drugs Act of 1906, and it is fair to conjecture that the nutritional value of foods were of little concern to those who drafted that legislation. Those legislators were interested rather in the economic factors of food misbranding and in the effect upon health of foods that were contaminated with filth, decomposed, or harmful because of the presence of toxic substances. At the time, knowledge of nutrition and the relation of food composition to the metabolism of animals and man was not sufficiently developed to serve as a guide to legislation.

At the beginning of the century the word "vitamin" had not been coined. The disease beriberi in man had been recognized for centuries, but its cause and cure were unknown. An analogous condition had been produced in chickens and was shown to be related to the food consumed. The concept of deficiency disease was in the making, and there was a growing acceptance of the value of small animal experimentation for developing new information about nutrition. It had not yet been demonstrated that the absence from the diet of a single amino acid would result in growth failure. It was not known to what extent the results obtained in experiments with animals of one species could be applied to other species.

In the period since 1906, the new science of nutrition has grown to maturity. A number of discoveries between 1910 and 1930 established that vitamins A, B, C, and D were essential for man. During the following decade, the isolation and synthesis of a number of vitamins was accomplished. These discoveries were followed by the development for the manufacture of vitamins of a large segment of the pharmaceutical industry. Discoveries in other fields have been equally spectacular to the scientist, but they have not led to the same degree of application that affects all consumers. We now know that there are 10 amino acids that are essential, and we look at the amino acid content of a food as well as the percentage of protein. But the only commercial application made so far of this knowledge has been in the feeding of poultry and swine.   Several trace minerals formerly considered only from the standpoint of possible toxicity are now known to be essential for man and other animals. At the present time, much of the nutrition research is directed toward demonstrating whether or not nutrition plays an important role in the progress of degenerative diseases, particularly of the blood vessels.

The Food, Drug, and Cosmetic Act became law in 1938 at a time when the commercial application of the rapidly increasing knowledge of nutrition was in its infancy. In this law, broad authority, which as yet has not been fully explored, is given to the Secretary to prescribe by regulations labeling requirements for foods for special dietary uses. The rapidity with which new facts about nutrition have been found and the procedural requirements of the law have combined to limit the extent to which effective regulatory control can be exercised over nutrition claims by means of prescribed labeling requirements.

Under this Act, regulations have been promulgated to control the labeling of a number of classes of foods that are important for supplementing the diet and also of foods that are intended for special uses. Through a regulatory program of enforcement in the Food and Drug Administration, the vitamin content of various products is determined, and a program of research gives assistance in evaluating claims made for beneficial effects alleged to be obtained by the use of vitamin preparations. Through cooperative effort on the part of industry, the *United States Pharmacopeia*, the Association of Official Agricultural Chemists, and food and drug laboratories, accurate methods for the determination of important constituents have provided a basis for production of high quality products and for a sound regulatory program.

Advance of the science of nutrition has been rapid, and new findings have provided additional avenues of exploitation by those interested only in profits. The almost universal appeal of the objective of good nutrition and the genuine importance of the advances made in scientific knowledge in this field have provided the clever copywriter with an unusual opportunity to prepare promotional material characterized by "scare techniques," "half truths," and gross exaggeration. Claims of benefit through the relief of vague symptoms that are common to many illnesses may be so cleverly stated that they are difficult to combat. Many users of a product having exaggerated claims are not prone to be critical when they see a product offered for the relief of "that tired feeling," a condition that may be advance notice of serious disease.

Regulation of the claims made for vitamins and other products of purported special dietary value presents a very difficult problem. While it has been possible to exert some pressure to keep the printed labels and labeling of these products from getting too far out of hand, the tremendous volume of other promotional material that is presented on television, radio, and other conventional advertising media, together with the word of mouth advertising of quack health lecturers, pitchmen, and house-to-house canvassers presents a regulatory problem of tremendous difficulty under present types of governmental controls. It does not seem to be good governmental practice to permit the present misuse of new scientific findings.

Thus there is much evidence that the education of the layman with respect to nutrition has not kept pace with scientific developments in nutrition. Some discoveries have been so spectacular that the uninformed person finds it difficult to differentiate between fact and fiction. This has made him vulnerable to misrepresentations. For example, he is constantly bombarded by statements concerning the losses of vitamins and minerals from foods, so that he becomes convinced that his diet is inadequate. The remedy offered is simply the use of a tablet or capsule that contains the nutrient he needs. Such promotional bombardment should be combated with sound nutrition education. We must see that proper nutrition information is placed in the hands of our educators, to be used in an effective program through schools and libraries. The less acceptable alternative may be a broader means of governmental control.

A Food Manufacturer Looks at the Food and Drug Administration

WALTER F. SILBERSACK

President, American Home Products Corporation
New York, N. Y.

To the American food manufacturer, 1956 will be a notable year, distinguished by two related events. First, June 30 will mark the golden anniversary of the enactment of our first Federal Food and Drugs Act. Second, by year-end our retail food buying is forecast to reach an all-time high of $71,000,000,000.

This record, one criterion of our people's better way of life, is a result of our democratic process of government by law. Basic among our Federal laws is the Federal Food, Drug, and Cosmetic Act as our national food law is known today. The food manufacturer considers this Act and its predecessor to have been significantly contributory to the health and social and economic progress of the last fifty years, and to be essential to protect and advance the interests of the public, and the medical profession and food industry which serve it.

This Act regulates foods involved in interstate commerce. Adulteration and misbranding of foods are prohibited, thereby assuring safety and purity and the honest, informative representation of them. This law was an accelerating factor in the orderly growth of our food economy during the last half century from essentially a local, individual effort to today's mass manufacturing and distribution with attendant benefits to the public. It forced the recognition, helped make available, and stimulated the use and advances of scientific principles in food manufacture. It provided the food industry with a safeguard to its integrity and reputation by relief from harmful and fraudulent competitive practices of a small minority segment of the industry.

Management in the food industry views our Federal food law, in part, as an instrument of the sciences and professions of nutrition and medicine, and consequently of value and utility to the practicing physician. Such value may be illustrated by four examples of typical application to the professional dietary management of foods.

First, the breadth of the definition of adulterated foods extends beyond the more obvious presence of poisonous or deleterious substance. For instance, valuable constituents may not be omitted or abstracted from a food. Neither may any substance be substituted wholly or partially for a food. Thus not only the safety of foods is protected, but also their integrity and composition, which help determine nutritive value.

Second, foods must be labeled honestly and informatively, which thus facilitates their economic and nutritional evaluation. Certain mandatory information must be declared on labels, including the true name of the food, its ingredients, the quantitative contents of the package in terms customarily used by the consumer, and the name and address of the manufacturer or distributor. Thus the consumer and his physician have ready access to detailed information that may be required for the control of medical problems of food involvement like allergies, dietary deficiencies, and others.

Third, certain foods may be standardized by regulations issued under the Federal food law as the need and desirability arise. A food standard creates an official specification for such food, which includes a specific name, and mandatory as well as optional ingredients in controlled amounts. Currently standards are fixed for many of our most frequently consumed foods, of which a few examples are breads, flours, macaroni products, canned fruits and vegetables, milk, cream, eggs, and oleomargarine. Most significantly, these standards provide for the nutritional enrichment of many of our major foods, which have been selected in conformance with the soundest principles of medicine and nutrition. Dietary management of the enriched foods is simplified with the knowledge that only such foods as conform to the official standard may be designated "enriched," that the quantity of the enriching ingredients are within safe and effective limits, and that their contribution to the minimum daily requirements is conveniently declared on the label.

Fourth, foods represented for special dietary uses must be labeled with particular specificity to convey full and concise dietary information as established by regulations issued from time to time. The regulation defines special dietary uses, in part, as "uses for supplying particular dietary needs which exist by reason of a physical, physiological, pathological or other condition, including but not limited to the conditions of disease, convalescence, pregnancy, lactation, allergenic hypersensitivity to food, underweight and overweight."

Typical examples of special dietary food uses are the low sodium foods prescribed for the treatment of certain heart, liver, and kidney diseases and high blood pressure. The regulation for such foods requires the uniform declaration of the sodium content in terms of milligrams of sodium in 100 Gm. of the food, and in the average serving of the food. Thus the intake of sodium is more readily and accurately calculated and controlled.

The brief and over-simplified interpretation of our Federal food law by the foregoing four examples is illustrative of its value to the physician by assurance of the availability of safe and dependable foods for the nourishment, prophylaxis, and therapy of the well and the diseased.

Additional appreciation of the benefits of the Federal Food, Drug and Cosmetic

Act in the food area of the public health and welfare is gained by some further, although incomplete indication of the breadth of its jurisdiction. This Act provides for the mandatory certification of all coal-tar colors for use in foods, the inspection of food plants and warehouses to prevent unsanitary conditions under which contamination might occur, the voluntary inspection and certification of seafoods, the regulation of imported foods, the seizure and harmless disposition of adulterated and misbranded foods to preclude their consumption by the public, and the punishment of violators.

The full realization of the value and benefits of the law depends entirely upon its continuous supplementation to keep pace with modern scientific and technologic progress and how effectively the law is administered.

As an example, in 1954 the Act was amended to establish exemptions or tolerances for pesticide residues in or on raw agricultural commodities or food in its raw or natural state. Of practical interest to the physician is the clearance by the Food and Drug Administration in November, 1955, under the 1954 amendment, of the first permissible use of an antibiotic, chlortetracycline, in the preservation of dressed, uncooked poultry. The permitted residue of this heat-labile antibiotic is destroyed by cooking. Thus, sensitization of the consumer to the antibiotic and the emergence of resistant strains of pathogenic microorganisms in the consumer is prevented. This new method of preservation reduces spoilage costs in the distribution and marketing of poultry and results in lower retail prices of benefit to the public.

Our Federal food law is administered by the Secretary of Health, Education, and Welfare through the Food and Drug Administration (FDA). The FDA consists of five administrative and eight technical divisions, which are Antibiotics, Cosmetics, Food, Medicine, Microbiology, Nutrition, Pharmaceutical Chemistry, and Pharmacology. The operating funds of the FDA are annually appropriated by Congress except for some self-liquidating income derived from industry-paid services. During the last few years, the annual appropriation has remained relatively unchanged at the rate of about .035 cents per capita. Last year a Citizens' Advisory Committee was appointed with the approval of Congress to assist in the evaluation of the performance and needs of the FDA. This Committee recognized the increasing burden on the FDA caused by our growing population and economy, and the quickening pace of science and technology. The question of the safety, nutritive value, and acceptability of foods exposed to atomic warfare or to radiation controlled for purposes of food sterilization and preservation is but one example. This Committee recommended a three- to fourfold increase of the operating budget over a period of 5 to 10 years and a separate appropriation to construct a modern headquarters building into which may be consolidated its now inefficiently separated housing.

It is the vital concern of every citizen, particularly those in the medical and food professions and industry, to be alert to the need of additional resources to the FDA. Through it are coordinated to the public the increasing benefits of our expanding medical and food sciences so essential to the security of our nation upon which rests the welfare of the free world.

The Milling Industry and the Federal
Food and Drug Administration

G. CULLEN THOMAS

Vice-President, General Mills, Inc.
Minneapolis, Minn.

That "the production of food is a public trust" is a concept that now has all but universal acceptance. It is most unusual these days to find anyone who will maintain the contrary.

It was not always thus. Fifty years ago, when Congress enacted the original Food and Drugs Act under the prodding of Harvey W. Wiley, there was widespread opposition. Many well-intentioned citizens maintained that by this action the Federal Government was presuming to regulate private business, an area where it had no right, no matter how laudable the objectives were. There also existed at that time within the food industries something of a fear that the "pure food cranks" would harass food manufacturers to such an extent that normal business processes would be disturbed and perhaps disrupted. These were not majority opinions, but they were common at that time.

How different was the attitude of nearly everyone concerned when Congress undertook 30 years later to revise the original Act! When this program was undertaken in the mid-thirties, the food industries generally supported the program of revision, which strengthened the law in many particulars and greatly amplified the powers that the administering agency possessed over the preparation, shipment, storage, and labeling of food products. This changed point of view largely grew out of the generally satisfactory experience that the food industry had under the original Act.

Like most other food manufacturers, we who are engaged in the milling of flour learned many years ago that any problem confronting our industry, which came within the purview of the Food and Drug Administration, received sympathetic consideration when it was presented honestly and fairly. It has been our observation that a succession of excellent Federal Food and Drug Commissioners and their staffs were invariably willing to talk over these problems carefully and help us find practical solutions, yet in compliance with the law. In these conferences, there never was any question about the public interest being paramount—that was and still is the main objective of the Food and Drug organization—but the officials nevertheless always seemed to be aware that solutions to be worthwhile had to be practical and not theoretical. It was in that kind of atmosphere where we have found answers over the years to such major problems of the milling industry as definitions and standards of identity for flour and other mill products, the flour bleaching controversy, the program of enrichment of flour with vitamins and iron, the activities of the food faddists, and the grain sanitation situation. These are several of the more important issues that have been considered jointly, mutually satisfactorily by the Food and Drug Administration and the flour milling industry.

It is an impressive fact that the Food and Drug Administration has relied chiefly upon educational processes to bring about reforms and improvements in food production, and on the whole has employed its police powers sparingly. While the statutes extend a generous grant of authority to compel observance of laws and regulations, the decided preference for educational processes to bring about compliance has been noteworthy, with, however, enough court action to demonstrate to the laggard and sometimes unwilling minority that they must live up to the requirements as do their more farsighted and progressive neighbors, and that what in the long run is in the best interest of the consumers is likewise good business policy.

It has not been necessary to be meekly compliant in order to enjoy a friendly cooperative relationship with the Food and Drug Administration. On more than a few occasions during the years, there have been honest differences of opinion between our industry and Food and Drug officials. Usually these differences have been settled by conference, with each side speaking its piece frankly. Sometimes the point of view of our industry has prevailed and sometimes not, but in no case have we found the Food and Drug Administration unwilling to give reasonable consideration to our point of view.

Looking to the future, it is the considered opinion of our industry that the welfare of food manufacturers depends as much upon having a strong Food and Drug Administration as it does upon any other factor. We are aware of the tremendous increase in the responsibilities of enforcement that is theirs today, and we are most happy to see evidences of an awakened public consciousness of the importance of all Food and Drug Administration activities. Just as the work of bank examiners has gradually created confidence in the banking institutions of our nation, so does the vigilance and integrity of the Food and Drug Administration establish in the public mind that the nation's food supply is safe and wholesome. This assurance is of vast importance to the people of the nation, but it is likewise a bulwark for progress and benefit for the future of the food industries.

When the first Food and Drugs Act went into effect half a century ago, the tremendous progress that it has fostered could not possibly have been forecast. It is now universally recognized and accepted that the American people enjoy the very best, most diversified, most nutritious, and safest foods of any nation in the world. It seems certain that today it would be equally impossible to predict what may ensue during the second half century of food and drug legislation and enforcement. However, we in the flour milling industry enthusiastically endorse a strong, cooperative, practical enforcement of our basic food laws as an essential to further progress.

Stilbestrol as a Possible Food Additive

JACK M. CURTIS
Chief, Endocrine Branch
Division of Pharmacology, Food and Drug Administration
Department of Health, Education, and Welfare
Washington, D. C.

Interest in the use of diethylstilbestrol as an additive to feeds for steers to produce an increase in rate of growth and an increase in the efficiency of utilization of food has grown very rapidly. In the last two years its use has become quite general. It has been reported that the increased rate of growth in steers fed stilbestrol at the rate of 10 mg. per day is approximately 20 per cent, and, concomitantly, there is a decrease of about 17 per cent in food intake per pound gain. The economic advantage of the use of diethylstilbestrol in feeding steers in feed lots is generally recognized.

The mechanism by which this change takes place is not clear. There is some evidence that stilbestrol, whether it be fed or whether it be administered in the form of pellet implants, increases the nitrogen retention. There is also evidence that this treatment produces a hypertrophy of the liver, the adrenal glands, and the pituitary without any specific cellular changes. These observations seem to indicate that there is a change in the endocrine gland metabolism, but exactly how these changes produce the increased growth rate and the increased efficiency of food utilization has not been clearly stated.

The Food and Drug Administration recognized the trend when it published on December 4, 1948, in the *Federal Register*, the general policy that in considering new drug applications for products intended to affect physiologic changes in farm animals, it would regard the absence of satisfactory evidence showing that the meat or other food obtained from animals fed such a drug is entirely free of any poisonous, deleterious ingredient resulting therefrom at the time of marketing as grounds for refusal to make the application effective. In line with this policy, prior to the general distribution of any stilbestrol-containing feed supplements, the Food and Drug Administration has required manufacturers to submit extensive evidence showing that there was no added estrogen in the edible part of steers fed diethylstilbestrol.

Several of the companies have developed assay techniques exhibiting sensitivities that are quite astonishing. It has been shown that meat from steers fed 10 mg. of stilbestrol per day when ready for market contains less than 2 parts per billion of added stilbestrol. Therefore it may be stated with considerable confidence that stilbestrol fed to steers under the conditions outlined by the manufacturers of feed supplements will constitute no hazard as an additive to food products derived from animals thus fed.

As a side issue to the general use of stilbestrol additives for steers, another problem relating to the occurrence of stilbestrol as a contaminant in feeds not intended for steers has arisen. On several occasions, feeds prepared for small laboratory animals have been run through mixers immediately following feeds prepared with stilbestrol for steers. The result has been an accidental contamination of the small animal feeds with stilbestrol. This contamination in some cases had quite serious effects upon the reproductive capacity of such small animal colonies.

The exact method of controlling such contamination and preventing its occurrence is under study by the Food and Drug Administration at the present time. It is hoped that methods of clearing mixing channels in food-mixing plants can be developed that will entirely prevent this most unjustifiable and hazardous occurrence.

The Use of Antibiotic Pesticides in Food for Human Consumption (Cooked or Uncooked)

W. B. RANKIN

Assistant to the Commissioner
Food and Drug Administration
Department of Health, Education, and Welfare
Washington, D. C.

Agriculturalists and food technologists continually seek new methods of combatting plant diseases and for retarding the spoilage of food after harvest. They have turned repeatedly to chemicals to aid food production and preservation. It is understandable that scientists are looking at the antibiotics as potentially useful tools of agriculture and food technology.

The antibiotics will control a variety of pests under proper conditions. They control some fungus diseases of plants. They destroy or inhibit the growth of many food spoilage organisms. However, there are potential dangers from the addition of antibiotics to food. These must be evaluated carefully, to guard against practices that jeopardize the public health. The U. S. Food and Drug Administration, which is responsible for safeguarding the food supply, states its views on this matter as follows: "The antibiotics are employed widely as drugs. In the doses used they sensitize some individuals. Sensitive people suffer a variety of adverse effects from further exposure to antibiotics which range from relatively mild discomfort to death."

Many pathogenic organisms become tolerant to the antibiotics when they are exposed to sublethal concentrations. Diseases caused by such resistant organisms often are more difficult to treat than those diseases caused by organisms susceptible to antibiotic therapy.

Another factor of importance is the problem of long-term or chronic toxicity. When used as drugs these chemicals are consumed by man in much higher quantities and for shorter intervals than would result from consumption of food treated in the ways now being considered. This does not mean, however, that the smaller quantities are nontoxic. Food is consumed daily over the lifetime of man. The safety of such lifetime consumption of antibiotics even of small amounts can be established only by lifetime feeding studies. These studies have to be made on test animals.

These chemicals are being considered for some uses that may leave them in food as it is eaten. Examples are their addition to chopped vegetable salads and pastry fillings to retard spoilage; the spraying of mature crop plants to control plant disease; and the preserving of certain seafoods and meats. Before uses of this type are permitted, there must be sound evidence that the added preservatives are safe. This requires facts about: (1) The ability of the concentrations that would be present to promote the development of drug resistant organisms, to sensitize individuals to the antibiotic drugs, and to cause reactions in persons already sensitized; (2) the cumulative toxicity of small doses repeated daily for the lifetime of test animals.

The antibiotics already are being used in food production under conditions that insure that they do not remain in the food we eat. Pear trees are sprayed at blossom time with a broad-spectrum antibiotic to control fire blight; seedling tomato plants are dipped in or sprayed with the chemicals to control fungus diseases. Because of the time between spraying and harvesting, none of the chemicals is present in the pears or tomatoes. Waste liquors from manufacturing plants are added to animal feeds to speed up growth of livestock; although these liquors have residual antibiotics, no chemical residue remains in the dressed carcass.

Chlortetracycline is used in the water in which poultry is chilled after dressing. Some of the chlortetracycline enters the poultry tissues where it retards spoilage. The Food and Drug Administration permits up to 7 parts per million of the chemical in uncooked poultry, because later cooking always destroys this amount of residue in this food.

The present status of the proposed uses of antibiotics in food is: (1) They may be used so that no residues remain in the food. This is acceptable. (2) They may be used so that residues remain in the uncooked food. This is acceptable provided the food is always cooked, since the cooking always destroys all of the antibiotic. An official tolerance has been set for the amount of residue that may remain, and the residue is within this tolerance. (3) They have been considered for uses that will leave some of the antibiotic in the food as it is eaten. Their safety under these conditions has not been established. They should not be used in this way until we know more about the effect of the residues on man and microorganisms that may cause disease.

Microscopic Detection of Food and Drug Adulteration

WILLIAM V. EISENBERG
*Division of Microbiology, Food and Drug Administration
Department of Health, Education, and Welfare
Washington, D. C.*

When the original Food and Drugs Act was passed 50 years ago, microscopy was an established tool for the analysis of food and drug products, particularly on the European continent. The well-known treatise by Andrew L. Winton, "The Microscopy of Vegetable Foods," appeared in 1906, the same year in which the original Food and Drugs Act was enacted. Thus, the compound microscope was one of the first analytic tools available to the forensic scientist for detection of adulteration in food and drug products. Under the microscope, the seemingly genuine appearance of a spurious substitute or mixture quickly vanished when the microscopic structure was revealed to the experienced observer. Analytic microscopy provides information relating to the nature and purity of food and drug products often unavailable from chemical analysis alone.

It is not surprising that the microscope came into use early in the enforcement of the Food and Drugs Act. The 1907 United States Department of Agriculture *Yearbook of Agriculture* carries an article by B. J. Howard entitled "The Use of the Microscope in the Detection of Food Adulteration." Among the products listed as amenable to this type of analysis for identifying the presence or addition of cheap adulterants were starch products, spices, coffee and chocolate preparations, jellies and jams, cream, edible fats, and honey. New applications developed rapidly. The quantitative microscopic procedure, known today as the "Howard mold count method," for the detection of decayed tomatoes in strained tomato products was published in 1911.

A marked change in the pattern of food and drug distribution has occurred during the 50 years of law enforcement. Manufacturing and processing operations gradually moved from the home or village shop to large factories. Increasingly, finished products on the market were so processed that neither the identity nor integrity of the ingredients were apparent to the consumer or regulatory analyst. The continuing adaptation and application of microscopic methods to the detection of adulteration of food and drug products thus became an important development in the Food and Drug Administration laboratories.

In the field of food adulteration, many new applications of the microscope have been introduced. An entirely new field of sanitation science has emerged from the application of microscopic methods to problems relating to filth and decomposition in foods and drugs. Quantitative microscopic methods have been developed for dealing with materials that may be decomposed, insect infested, rodent infested, or contaminated by other materials that may have gotten into the finished products. By means of these procedures, it is possible to make counts of mold filaments, insect fragments, rodent hairs, or other criteria of adulteration and correlate the results obtained with the cleanliness and soundness of the raw materials used or with good or bad sanitary conditions in the factories where the products are manufactured. The microscope also affords a ready means of control that can be carried on during the process of manufacture. For the past decade, each successive edition of *Methods of Analysis* of the Association of Official Agricultural Chemists has carried an entire chapter of microscopic methods devoted to the detection of filth and decomposition in foods and drugs. Most of these methods have been developed during the past 20 years.

The early part of this century saw the increased development and growth of microscopy utilizing the principles of animal and plant histology for the identification of ingredients of food and drug products derived from these tissues. In the laboratories of the Food and Drug Administration, the microscopy of food and drug products has involved the study of a large group and variety of materials and substances. A vast catalogue of material and significant data for the identification of food and drug ingredients has been compiled.

Although there are many applications of microscopic identification techniques to foods, e.g., to check declared composition and to detect the substitution of inferior or spurious ingredients, major developments have been connected with drugs. Considerable work in this field was accomplished in the Food and Drug Administration laboratories when drugs of plant or animal origin occupied a considerable part of the official and nonofficial drug compendia. The last several decades have seen many of the relatively crude drugs obtained from plant and animal tissues replaced by their active chemical principles or by synthetic chemical substances. Along with this trend came the use of polarized light microscopy to deal with crystalline chemical substances and the introduction of many new techniques in the field of chemical microscopy. Optical crystallographic methods (polarized light microscopy) and chemical microscopic tests are invaluable in food and drug work for identification of small quantities of material rapidly and specifically.

Microscopy has played an important part in the regulation of food and drug products and has contributed substantially to the reputation for purity and wholesomeness that these products enjoy in the United States and throughout the world.

Carcinogenic Substances in Foods

A. A. NELSON
Chief, Pathology Branch
Division of Pharmacology, Food and Drug Administration
Department of Health, Education, and Welfare
Washington, D. C.

This editorial is written neither by nor for an expert cancer worker. Instead, it is written by a general pathologist for the general medical reader.

With the (1) ever-increasing tendency toward "chemicalization" of foods, (2) the increased number of minute amounts of contaminating chemicals such as pesticides, and (3) the increasing tempo of cancer research, the possible role of the diet and its contaminants in relation to cancer has an understandable interest. The term "chemicals" in relation to food is a reasonable one. True, food was composed of chemicals even in primitive days, but in everyday language "chemical" refers to the more purified and synthetic components and contaminants of food rather than to the naturally occurring chemical agglomerations present.

It should be noted immediately that the subject "carcinogenic substances in foods" is a much less inclusive one than "nutrition and cancer." The former, in a strict sense, leaves out consideration of the cancer itself, dietary influence on a cancer after it has become established, and dietary influence in restraining the potential activity of endogenous carcinogens and endogenous aiding factors. This brief discussion will hold rather closely to its title; in other words, it concerns cancer from nutrition rather than nutrition affecting cancer.

Does the diet, with its possible carcinogenic content, influence the incidence of human cancer? About this we know essentially nothing because of the lack of the necessary statistical data and because of the multiplicity of factors involved. Once human cancer is established, dietary influence of any consequence upon it is not known. In contrast, the incidence of certain animal tumors, particularly the rat liver tumors caused by azo compounds, is highly influenced by dietary variations, and once established, animal tumors are still influenced. It should be understood that caloric variation is included in the term "dietary variation."

Specifically, then, as to actual substances: Heated (and overheated) fats, and to a lesser extent roasted foods, have been among the most studied food items with respect to experimental cancer production. While they have often been heated to a greater degree than would normally occur, this is a reasonable trial technique. The important point, however, is whether there has been a definite production of cancer by the feeding of such substances. It is at least an open question. A careful reading of the published evidence leads to the reasonable conclusion that the amount claimed is greater than the amount not accounted for by parasitism, chance occurrence, or malnutrition. By the nature of the treatment of the food item, it is most difficult or even impossible to have a material that differs from the untreated material only by the presence of a single chemical compound. In some experiments, the feeding of heated fat has been complicated by the additional feeding of such substances as croton oil, pepper, or soap. Even subcutaneous injection of heated fat, the control animals being injected with unheated fat, does not get away from variables; there are physical differences, such as viscosity, that can affect the results, and greater retention of heated fat than of unheated fat at injection sites has been noted. It would seem that heated fat feeding studies may be summarized by saying that a low grade of tumor production has occasionally been achieved. More important, and only beginning, is the chemical characterization of the responsible agents, and the realization of how seemingly insignificant differences in treatment (e.g., heating in an iron as contrasted to a glass container) may change the character of the heated material.

Considerable concern has been expressed about the possibility of colors and insecticide residues in food being carcinogenic. A minimal degree of liver tumor production in rats is known for dichlorodiphenyltrichloroethane (DDT) and certain other insecticides. However, the amounts needed to do this are much greater than the amounts ingested as residue by man, and, because of this safety factor, the minimal degree of rat tumor production is not alarming. However, when an insecticide is a distinct tumor producer, as for example selenium, the situation is different.

The only food colors considered here are the 19 certifiable Food, Drug, and Cosmetic colors used for food coloring in the United States. None of these has as yet shown evidence of carcinogenicity in man or in feeding tests with experimental animals. Some, particularly in the triphenylmethane class, have produced fibrosarcomas at the site of repeated subcutaneous injections in rats. This site, known to be a sensitive one and only recently coming into common use in carcinogenicity testing, is of course an abnormal one as far as food colors in the diet are concerned. To the extent that time and limited facilities permit, the Food and Drug Administration is engaged in more detailed animal toxicity studies with these colors than has heretofore been done. Partially as a suggestion to other researchers who are concerned with possible food color carcinogenicity, it should be noted that five of the 19 colors together account for more than 80 per cent of use, and eight of them together account for less than 2 per cent of use.

Has any single carcinogenic substance been isolated from "natural," uncontaminated human foods? The answer must yet be "no," because although certain foods (chili peppers, Hoch-Ligeti; buckwheat, Kubo et al) have caused liver tumors in rats and mice respectively, the tumor formation has not been shown to be dependent upon a single chemical substance. The "uncontaminated" leaves out crude ergot, a contaminant of rye, which caused neurofibromas of the ears in rats (Nelson et al).

Substances that have been found to be carcinogenic (rat liver tumors) in recent years, and that for that and other reasons the Food and Drug Administration has tried to keep out of foods, include dulcin, thiourea, and compounds of selenium. These were, respectively, a synthetic sweetener, a preservative, and insecticides. As new chemicals and new uses for old ones are developed, some of these will no doubt also be found carcinogenic.

The foregoing has presented some of the highlights in a complex and many-faceted problem.

Heated Fats

ANNE R. BOURKE

Pharmacologist, Chronic Toxicity Branch
Division of Pharmacology, Food and Drug Administration
Department of Health, Education, and Welfare
Washington, D. C.

The disquieting suspicion that some relatively simple factor or factors to which we are universally, unknowingly exposed might be contributing to the high cancer incidence in the population has occurred to both lay and scientific minds. Pathologic reports, when analyzed from a geographic and sociologic aspect, have indicated that environmental factors play a greater part than do hereditary or racial factors. This appears to be notably true of cancers of the stomach. For years there has been a lurking fear that we may be unwittingly consuming carcinogenic substances in our daily diets.

Such fears seemed to have been justified in 1939 when the Argentine scientist Roffo reported that malignant growths were induced in the stomachs of rats by the inclusion of large quantities of heated fats in the diet. The experimental diets contained animal fats and vegetable oils in common dietary usage that were heated at 350 C (662 F), a temperature attainable in certain phases of frying and roasting methods, for 30 minutes. This report followed the reports of Peacock in 1933 and Kennaway in 1936 that heated fats could act as carcinogens when injected into the subcutaneous tissues of rats and mice.

It has been estimated that at least one fourth of the deaths from cancer in the white population are due to cancers of the stomach. It has also been estimated that two thirds of the fat in the diets of civilized populations is consumed as heated fat. It is therefore understandable that Roffo's findings aroused widespread interest and sparked a flurry of activity in cancer research and lipid chemistry. If heated fats could produce cancer in the glandular portion as well as in the fore-stomach of animals notably resistant to cancers of this particular tissue, how much more damage might be invoked in the almost entirely glandular stomach of man, the most susceptible species. Carcinogenicity of heated fats offered a simple and logical explanation for one of the great scourges of man.

Unfortunately the explanation has not proved to be that simple. Since 1939, at least a dozen workers in cancer research have attempted, without success, to reproduce Roffo's results. Beck and Peacock (1941) in Glasgow; Morris, Larsen, and Lippincott (1943) of the National Cancer Institute; and Lane, Blankenship, and Ivy (1950) at Chicago, are among those who have been unable to produce malignant changes in glandular portion of rodent stomachs by the feeding of heated fats. Papillomas of the rat forestomach, a tissue which has no counterpart in man, were obtained but were associated with vitamin A deficiency rather than direct carcinogenic effect of heated fats.

Although it is at present concluded that the consumption of heated fats is not the cause of gastric cancer in man, interest in the changes brought about in lipids by heat is still very much alive. In the course of experiments in which heated lipids were fed, it was noted that under some test conditions heated oils retarded animal growth. During and after World War II, in order to supplement the dietary fat supply, it became advisable in some countries to investigate the possibility of converting nonedible fats to edible fats. Highly unsaturated vegetable oils and some fish oils that are subject to odor and flavor changes when exposed to light and heat were rendered more stable by thermal polymerization. However, it became evident that heat polymerization of some of these oils reduced their nutritional value and could produce substances that are toxic in themselves. Lipid chemists in several universities, in industrial research, and at the Food and Drug Administration are attempting to isolate and identify the toxic component of the heated material.

Progress is understandably slow. Each oil behaves in an individual fashion according to the amount and kind of fatty acids contained in its glyceride esters. Each fatty acid reacts differently according to the degree of unsaturation. The end products of heating each oil will differ according to conditions of temperature, time, presence or absence of oxygen, presence or absence of natural or added antioxidants, traces of chlorophyl, presence of catalysts, and even surface area during heat treatment.

The Food and Drug Administration would like definite answers to a few important questions. One has only to think of the processes involved in the commercial production of potato chips, doughnuts and various baked goods, and of practices in the kitchens of large restaurants to realize that we all consume a small quantity of lipid that has been heated for long periods of time (as much as 200 hours in some cases) at high temperatures and in metal containers that allow a wide surface for contact with air. Therefore, the questions become obvious. Is there a true toxic entity in heated fats? If a toxic product is present, what is its chemical nature? Is the apparent heat damage to nutritive value of fats due to destruction of vitamins A or E? Which oils are most susceptible to detrimental changes by heat? What type of cooking vessels minimize thermal changes of oils? Is there any danger, however slight, in modern food production methods involving certain oils? And finally, back to that earlier suspicion, are there perhaps substances in certain heated oils that can act as weak carcinogens?

The solution to many of these questions depends upon the chemists' success in separating the products of heated oils into chemically definable compounds. Recent studies consist chiefly of treating oils of known composition by thermal, oxidative or thermal oxidative polymerization methods, separating the products into various fractions by distillation techniques and chemical methods, and the testing of each fraction for toxicity to animals. Ultimately a fraction shown to be toxic may be broken down to yield a specific toxic chemical entity. At that time, the pharmacologist, who must make the final decision regarding the safety of heated fats and oils in commercially produced dietary items, will be on firm ground.

Radioactive Fallout and Our Food Supply

EDWIN P. LAUG

Chief, Physiochemistry Branch
Division of Pharmacology, Food and Drug Administration
Department of Health, Education and Welfare
Washington, D. C.

The term "radioactive fallout" brings to the minds of most people an association either with our own testing of nuclear weapons and devices or the eventual possibility of enemy action. This is only one side of the coin. Within the next 10 years, there will probably be numerous industrial applications of nuclear power, some perhaps as yet poorly defined. Many of the waste products of nuclear reactions are radioactive, and, while proper engineering devices can be undoubtedly set up to prevent most atmospheric contamination in the manner of fallout, there will still remain a problem of increasing urgency on disposal.

We have then the problem of adding to our environment a new potential for contamination, whether of the air, water, or soil. Actually, in the long run, it does not make too much difference whether this contamination will be controlled and diluted, or whether it may be concentrated in some areas due to overt action.

The number of ways in which contamination of our food supply by fallout can occur are: (1) through contamination of finished products stored or in transit, the degree varying considerably with type of packaging and storage; (2) through contamination of air or water used in the processing of food products; (3) through the external contamination of crops in the field; and (4) through the internal contamination of plants and animals translocating radioactivity from soil, water, or air.

What is the relative importance of these avenues of contamination, and what can be done to prevent such contamination? Taking them in order, it may be said, generally, that there is considerable hope in controlling contamination of finished food products. For example, bulk storage products could be "skimmed" in order to salvage the deeper layers. From experience with other types of disasters, the cleaning of the surfaces of cans, glass jars, and bottles may be feasible. In the case of forewarned enemy action, certain preventive measures, such as removal or covering of vulnerable items, could even be attempted. It is not envisioned that this type of contamination would arise from properly engineered industrial nuclear facilities. Accidents, of course, could happen, but it is believed that their impact would be minor.

With respect to the second item, namely, contamination of air and water used in processing food, it is believed that tight control of filtration processes could effect removal of radioactivity to satisfactory low levels. Here, certainly, the economics of industrial processes would enter; nevertheless, as our information on the dangers to health from radioactivity becomes more clearly defined, reasonable safety limits and standards will be set up. These might even be applicable in the event water and air had been contaminated by enemy action.

The over-all picture of surface contamination of crops and the eventual uptake of radioactivity from their environment by plants and animals is gloomy. Accounts of the recent Pacific tests and the subsequent dramatization in a national weekly have brought home very forcibly the fact that vast areas of terrain may be contaminated by fallout. Here again considerable reliance might be placed on meteorologic forecasts defining areas of fallout, but it would be poor consolation to know that huge acreages of growing crops could not be protected, their product rendered inedible, and ground on which they grew, suspect.

It has been said that the best weapon against fallout is time, but of course this is only true if we can afford to wait until the radioactive elements in fallout have decayed to harmless levels. Most of them are relatively short lived, decaying to a fraction of their original activity in a few days. Radioactive strontium, however, is an unfortunate exception. It has a half life of 25 years. In chemical behavior it is similar to calcium; hence, it may find its way into bone structures or plant tissues. There is some evidence that the concentration of strontium in fallout may not be uniform; hence, when decisions must be made as to whether to condemn contaminated foodstuffs, such as truck crops, radiologic analysis, if economically feasible, should be attempted to determine the level of strontium.

If fallout contaminates the ground, the decision as to which crops to plant, which will not translocate strontium for example, is dependent on the development of a body of ecologic knowledge. Some of this information is already at hand, plus the very important finding that the uptake of strontium from the soil is materially reduced in the presence of adequate liming.

Paradoxically, the slow increase in the radioactivity of our environment, particularly soil and water, through industrial effluvia may be more significant than local areas of high contamination produced by overt enemy action. For the present, filter systems, catch basins, and the practice of large dilution by river systems seems adequate. In the future, large scale concentrating processes may be developed so that fixed radioactivity could be sunk in the ocean depths.

For the present, it does not appear that our general environment has been very significantly increased with respect to radioactivity. This is in spite of certain scare stories that have appeared in the press. Fallout dosage rate in the United States on January 1, 1955, was, according to Libby, 1 milliroentgen per year. This figure obviously makes an insignificant contribution to the natural dosage that ranges from 50 to 500 milliroentgen per year and results from cosmic rays, natural radioactivity in the soil and air, and radioactive potassium in our bodies.

It seems reasonable to assume, barring atomic warfare, that there will be a slow increase in the level of radioactivity in our environment, whether from industrial processes or continued nuclear weapon testing. Eventually an equilibrium point will be reached; this will be determined by the rate of decay of the longest-lived man-made radioactive species and their rate of replenishment. It is impossible at this time to assess the significance of this environmental increase in radioactivity, but the present estimates would place it on a par with wearing a luminous dial wrist watch and far below the exposure incurred from medical roentgenography. By such criteria, the question of mass radioactive poisoning through contamination of food supply now or in the near future is quite academic.

Hamburger—One Horse, One Cow

WILLIAM A. RANDALL

Food and Drug Administration
Division of Antibiotics
Washington, D. C.

Horse meat is used as food for human consumption in this country and many other parts of the world. However, when unscrupulous operators illegally substitute it for beef or mix it with beef or beef products to prepare hamburger or frankfurters, or similar products, it is a violation of Federal law if the adulterated product moves interstate and of State laws if it moves intrastate. Indeed, in California the adulteration of beef with horse meat constitutes a felony.

The motive for selling horse meat as beef is one of the most compelling in the world—greed and avarice. In one instance, choice tenderloins of horse could be bought for $0.20/lb. and sold for $1.00/lb. when falsely represented as beef, a nice margin of profit and one that allowed considerable leeway in competitive bidding with beef processors.

Early in 1950 investigations in Illinois uncovered a ring of horse meat racketeers whose operations extended as far as Texas and Florida. The exposure of this activity served to focus the attention of Federal and State authorities on this problem in their respective jurisdictions.

Now, most persons can tell a horse from a cow when viewed side by side, but when they have been killed and made into steaks or hamburgers, the most discerning cannot tell the difference, either by appearance or by taste. This posed a problem for State enforcement agencies who needed proof that suspect products were horse meat and, further, such evidence had to stand up in court. There is a test for horse meat that fulfills these requirements—the ring precipitin test first described by Rudolf Kraus in 1897. This is an immunologic test that has been used for many years for the medicolegal identification of blood stains but also occasionally for the detection of adulteration. Most State laboratories were not equipped to perform this test, so the Food and Drug Administration, through its Division of State Cooperation and the Division of Antibiotics, undertook to test samples sent in by the states. The cost of this testing program was borne by the Federal Government. To date, 1259 samples have been tested, of which 281 (24.1 per cent) were positive. The success of the State-Federal collaborative effort is attested by the fact that from May, 1950, to June, 1952, 1122 samples were tested, while since that time only 137 samples have been submitted. While constant vigilance is necessary, it may be confidently stated that major operations in this trafficking have been abandoned.

During the course of these investigations, a curious fact emerged—the vast majority of the American people do not like to eat horse meat. During the racing season at Laurel, Md., it was announced in the newspapers that a Baltimore firm was selling hot dogs containing horse meat. Consumption that day dropped from 40,000 to 40! Again, in Arkansas a minor economic crisis was created when a horse meat operator was exposed. The people stopped eating all kinds of meat and took to beans and cheese. Today it may be safely stated that the substitution of horse meat for beef is under control, and it is the temper of the American public to bet on or to ride horses, not to eat them.

Control of Seafood Shipped in Interstate Commerce

L. R. SHELTON, JR.

Division of Microbiology
Food and Drug Administration
Washington, D. C.

The seafood industry plays an important role in the production of food for the American consumer. In 1953, the total production of all types of seafoods was 4700 million pounds, having a retail market value of approximately $800,000,000. In common with other food industries, certain production problems are aggravated by uncertainties of fishing operations, the perishable nature of the raw materials, the vicissitudes of handling and transportation for the fresh or frozen product, and the confusion sometimes surrounding proper labeling. These combine to create problems of food law enforcement that brings the Food and Drug Administration squarely into the picture of fishery production and distribution.

The Food, Drug, and Cosmetic Act, while designed primarily as a consumer protection measure, also serves to protect the conscientious packer from the unfair practices of the minority fringe who have no feeling of responsibility for the integrity of their product. The consumer is entitled to a product prepared from fresh, clean, sound raw materials handled in a sanitary manner and properly labeled to designate clearly what the product is.

A seafood product or any other food is considered to be adulterated if it contains any poisonous or deleterious substance that may render it injurious to health; if it consists in whole or in part of any filthy, putrid, or decomposed substance, or if it is otherwise unfit for food; or if it has been prepared, packed, or held under insanitary conditions whereby it may have become contaminated with filth or rendered injurious to health.

Certain species of shellfish (clams, sea mussels) may contain a toxic substance derived from a planktonic organism upon which the shellfish feed. Consumption of such toxic shellfish may cause illness or even death; therefore, areas known to produce toxic shellfish are carefully monitored, and shipments are assayed for toxic properties. Similarly, imports of shellfish from areas known to have a toxicity problem are checked prior to admission into the United States.

Seafoods may be prepared and offered in commerce in a variety of ways. They may be fresh, frozen, canned, salted, dried, or smoked. In addition, a number of new products have appeared in which the fish or shellfish is coated with other ingredients to form a distinctive item. Fish sticks and breaded shrimp are examples of such preparations. For any of the various forms the raw materials are extremely perishable and must be handled rapidly and under adequate refrigeration if decomposition is to be avoided. Present day facilities for catching, refrigerating, preserving, and shipping are such that only an occasional lot of decomposed fish should appear in commerce and then only through inadvertence beyond the packer's control or through carelessness on the part of the packer or distributor.

Some species of fish are susceptible to infestation by parasites that form a repulsive cyst within the flesh. Fish so infested are considered contaminated with filth and are in violation of the law.

Seafood products must be labeled with the common or usual name of the fish or shellfish. Because of the loose usage of common names for fishes, the selection of a label designation is not always easy. The name should not mislead and should be in keeping with the biologic classification of the animal. The name under which a fish is offered for sale should be that which is customary, prevailing, universal, familiar, and popular in the sense that it is widely used and, hence, is accepted as the common or usual name.

In the course of their duties, inspectors of the Food and Drug Administration make factory inspections of food-producing establishments, including seafood plants. These inspections include a check on the quality of the raw materials, adequacy of sorting, sanitary conditions relating to operating procedures, and propriety of labels used on the finished product. In addition to this form of regulatory control, the Administration is authorized to provide a continuous, supervisory inspection to plants producing seafood products. This continuous inspection is provided for those seafood plants requesting it and able to meet the Government's requirements for sanitation and adequate control. It is supported by fees charged against the inspected establishment. Plants operating under this inspection may use an inspection legend on the label of the product. Currently, some plants canning shrimp and oysters are utilizing the inspection service.

The provisions of the Food, Drug, and Cosmetic Act apply equally to foods in interstate commerce within the United States and to foods offered for entry into this country. In the case of fresh or frozen shellfish (oysters, clams, mussels) produced domestically, the safeguards provided by the Act are augmented by a voluntary control program administered by the United States Public Health Service. Because of the special problems involved, this program is based upon control at the growing areas and production centers rather than upon the objective examination of the finished product as found in commerce. This control program deals primarily with the bacteriologic quality of the product at the source and does not absolve the product from full compliance with the food and drug law.

Prevention and Control of Food Poisoning

GLENN G. SLOCUM
Chief, Division of Microbiology
Food and Drug Administration
Washington, D. C.

The Food, Drug, and Cosmetic Act of 1938 is basically a statute to protect the public health. An important and continuing responsibility of the Food and Drug Administration, the agency charged with enforcement of the Act and of the original pure food law enacted 50 years ago, is the prevention and control of injuries produced by foods—"food poisoning" in its broadest sense.

The law defines a food as adulterated if it bears or contains a poisonous or deleterious substance that may render it injurious to health; if it consists in whole or in part of any filthy, putrid, or decomposed substance; if it has been prepared, packed, or held under insanitary conditions whereby it may have been rendered injurious to health; if it is the product of a diseased animal or of an animal that has died otherwise than by slaughter; or if its container is composed of any poisonous or deleterious substance that may render its contents injurious to health. Thus, the law provides a basis for the control of foods in interstate commerce adulterated by pathogenic microorganisms or their toxic products, by chemical poisons, by poisonous plants, or of inherently poisonous foods. Compliance with these requirements by processors and distributors should minimize injury to consumers.

Violations of the Act involving hazards to health are given the highest priority by the Food and Drug Administration. All outbreaks or cases of illness in which food is shown or suspected as the cause of injury are investigated promptly and violative products recalled and removed from the market to protect the public.

Foods shipped in interstate commerce are now infrequently implicated in food poisoning. Commercially canned foods have been virtually eliminated as sources of botulism, and outbreaks of gastroenteritis, characterized as staphylococcal intoxications or *Salmonella* infections, are rarely traced to foods shown to have been hazardous at the time of shipment. Enforcement programs and advances in food technology, in food plant sanitation, and in methods of food processing have resulted in the safest, cleanest food supply ever available to consumers.

The pattern of food production has changed substantially in the past 25 years. Whereas foods formerly were grown, processed, and consumed locally, food production is now largely concentrated in strategic locations according to the availability of raw materials, and the finished products are distributed nationally. Accidents or errors that result in the preparation of a harmful food may hazard consumers in widespread areas.

Improvements in environmental sanitation during this century have been reflected by pronounced decreases in morbidity and mortality rates for enteric disease. The Public Health Service has reported marked decreases in the incidence of outbreaks of water-borne and milk-borne diseases since 1940. However, the number of reported outbreaks of food poisoning increased substantially during the same period. While better reporting may explain part or most of this increase, it is clear that the factors responsible for the decrease in water- and milk-borne outbreaks have not operated to reduce the incidence of food poisoning.

Annual reviews of food poisoning by the Food and Drug Administration and other agencies reveal a common history of food mishandling, contamination, and infection at the time of preparation for serving, often by the consumer himself. Poor food-handling practices, food preparation by persons with skin infections, and failure to refrigerate food adequately are reported as factors contributing to a large proportion of food poisoning incidents.

It is generally agreed that an annual total of about 10 to 12 thousand cases of food poisoning reported in recent years represents a small proportion of the total cases, and it is believed that actual cases number several hundred thousands yearly. There is no room for complacency with respect to this distinct public health problem.

Food poisoning is a preventable disease. Progress in the eradication or reduction of such illnesses will require: (1) more effective education of food handlers, including the consuming public, in the fundamentals of hygienic food handling; (2) prompt and complete reporting of food-borne disease; and (3) more adequate epidemiologic and laboratory investigation of outbreaks to establish the source and etiologic agents. The reason for effective education of food handlers is clear. It is quite apparent that reporting is grossly inadequate, and often reports of outbreaks are delayed until it is too late to obtain the food or clinical specimens necessary to establish the etiology or epidemiology of the outbreak. There is a distinct need for better epidemiologic and laboratory tools for food poisoning investigations, but the use of existing facilities and techniques is too often neglected.

The Food and Drug Administration will press its program to prevent the distribution in interstate commerce of foods containing poisonous or deleterious substances. The problem is of such magnitude as to require the joint efforts of health officials at all levels, of the medical profession, and of the consuming public to reduce food poisoning as a public health problem.

V. FOOD AND DRUG ADMINISTRATION AND THE LAW

Fifty Years of Public Protection under Federal Food and Drug Laws

HENRY A. LEPPER
Department of Health, Education, and Welfare
Food and Drug Administration
Washington, D. C.

The Federal Food and Drugs Act of 1906 was not the first Federal law designed to control adulteration or misrepresentation of foods and drugs. In 1848 a law was passed prohibiting the importation of adulterated drugs and a similar one for foods in 1890. Several Acts of Congress, based upon the taxing authority, controlling specific foods were enacted before 1906. A few are still in effect. Some have been repealed. It was with the 1906 Act that the constitutional authority over interstate commerce vested in the Federal Government was utilized as the basis of a major regulatory law. That law dealt with foods and drugs, applying broad concepts of adulteration and misbranding designed to protect the public in three fundamental respects—health, esthetics, and welfare.

The first of these is, of course, of greatest importance. With foods, protection of health was accomplished by prohibition of deleteriousness or harmfulness. With drugs, health was guarded by requirements of purity, quality, and strength. Health also was to be protected by prohibition of false therapeutic claims on patent medicines. Promises of curative virtues without merit often result in a fatal delay of treatments of established effectiveness. Man's esthetic demand for clean and sound food was to be assured by a ban of contamination with filth and illegalizing decomposition in foods. To these major spheres of enforcement the other restrictions on adulteration and misbranding were designed to assure the consumer's welfare by preventing his being cheated. No longer was the purchaser dependent upon his limited ability to evaluate the honesty of the foods and drugs bought. He was protected against economic adulterations and, because of truthful labeling, could buy products for what they were.

As the years went by, successive interpretations by the judiciary made it obvious that as an instrument of jurisprudence the original law did not offer that measure of public protection which its sponsors had envisioned. The limitations placed on enforcement were numerous. Citation of several may serve to illustrate how ineffectiveness of enforcement developed. In the realm of health, to keep poisonous or harmful substances out of food, it became necessary to prove the food itself was injurious. This, most often, was forensically impossible. Again, to restrict false therapeutic claims on patent medicines, it became necessary to prove the claims were fraudulently made. To do so was equivalent to proving what the instigator of the claims was thinking. To condemn foods because of filthy contamination, the amount of filth to be found had to be shocking and repulsive. Less than such amount was regarded as accidental. There was no provision for classing the food as adulterated when it was prepared, packed, or held under insanitary conditions whereby it may have become contaminated with filth or rendered injurious to health. These and other shortcomings of protection of the public led to the passage of the Federal Food, Drug, and Cosmetic Act of 1938, which replaced the old law of 1906.

This new law was designed to correct weaknesses of the original and at the same time preserve those provisions of demonstrated effectiveness. By it, regulatory control was extended to cosmetics by applying the fundamental principles controlling adulteration and misbranding. Also, many new special features were added, such as the inclusion of devices under the definitions of adulterated and misbranded drugs and the augmentation of those definitions; the restriction of over-the-counter dispensing of drugs of stated potentialities without prescription from a practitioner licensed by law to administer such drugs; the prohibition of the marketing of new drugs until after the approval of an application to be permitted to do so; the authorizing of factory inspections; the providing for the promulgation of standards for foods having the force and effect of law; the requirement for more informative labeling on foods and drugs, notably a declaration of ingredients; and the compulsory certification of coal-tar dyes for use in foods, drugs, and cosmetics. The new law sets up specific procedures for a number of its judicial and administrative functions.

In the new law the seizure and prosecution provisions are retained and, in addition, procedure by injunction is specifically authorized. This feature is designed to prevent the exposure of the public to violative products rather than to depend upon seizure for their removal from channels of trade. Often some if not all of the goods become distributed to consumers before seizure can be consummated. These attempts at improving the law in the interest of consumer protection, as far reaching as they appear to be, were soon found short of the full public service intended. Accordingly, the Act has been amended on several occasions. Provision has been added for compulsory certification of drugs containing insulin and certain antibiotics. The food standardization procedure has been simplified. Control of residues of harmful pesticides is provided in an amendment for the setting of tolerances for pesticide chemicals that are used in or on raw agricultural commodities.

An amendment of far reaching significance, although a phrase of very few words, was the introduction of "or while held for sale (whether or not the first sale)" extending jurisdiction for goods subject to seizure. This amendment sets aside the old concept that foods and drugs are beyond the provisions of the law when coming to rest in the State to which they are shipped. It means that the jurisdiction is extended until the goods are purchased by the ultimate consumer. Congress at the time of passage included a section expressing the intent of extending the control over interstate commerce to carry protection to the final purchaser and consumer by prohibiting alteration, mutilation, destruction, obliteration, or removal of all or any part of the labeling while the article is held for sale. To express more clearly this intent, the phrase "(whether or not the first sale)" was added after the word "sale" in this section at the time it was added to the seizure section. A further broadening of authority over interstate commerce is provided in the oleomargarine amendment wherein products of intrastate origin are brought within the restrictions.

The 50 years of enforcement of the so-called food laws with the many amendments aimed at increased consumer protection have resulted in widespread consumer confidence when dealing for foods and drugs in the market place. This confidence has been a factor in the changed buying habits from the old open container system of distribution to that of present day manufactured and packaged commodities. The public largely assumes that everything it buys is safe, clean, and truthfully and informatively labeled. It is the enforcement official's responsibility to make and keep it so.

86

How the Law Protects Your Prescription

MALCOLM R. STEPHENS

Associate Commissioner of Food and Drugs
Department of Health, Education, and Welfare
Washington, D. C.

A well-known physician recently stated that one of the areas in medicine in which perfection is expected is in the formulation of drugs. It is reasonable to concede that the more seriously ill the patient, the more likely he is to apply that strict rule of conduct to all those who play a part in furnishing him the medication vital to his well-being.

The drug manufacturer, the pharmacist, and the regulatory official all recognize and accept this great public responsibility that is placed upon them. The enforcement official can meet his responsibility only through fair and efficient enforcement of the law he is given to administer. If he administers the law well, he meets his public responsibility to the extent that the objectives of the law satisfy the demands of a discerning public.

It becomes necessary then to examine the objectives of the Federal Food, Drug, and Cosmetic Act, as spelled out in the various statutory provisions relating to drugs, to determine whether or not they furnish the strict yardstick the physician wishes applied to the medicines he must administer.

Broadly speaking, the objectives of this law as applied to prescription drugs are that they be safe and of the composition and dosage professed in their labeling or otherwise. The so-called "prescription drugs" are those that are not safe for use without the supervision of a physician or other practitioner authorized by law to administer the drug. It is, of course, this class of drugs that is so vital to the person afflicted with a serious disease. Such drugs are required to bear the legend "Caution: Federal law prohibits dispensing without prescription," and they may not be legally sold without prescription.

The following are some of the more important requirements of the Food, Drug, and Cosmetic Act designed to assure that the patient gets "what the doctor ordered" when his prescription is filled:

"New drugs must not be marketed before an application establishing safety has been filed and has become effective.

"Drugs containing insulin, penicillin, streptomycin, bacitracin, Aureomycin (chlortetracycline), or chloramphenicol must not be marketed until they have been certified as safe and efficacious.

"A drug sold under an official name or under circumstances creating the impression that it is an official drug must comply with the official requirements except that it may differ from the official requirements in strength, quality, or purity only. If it does so differ, the label must indicate the nature and extent of each such difference. Difference from official specifications in the identity of ingredients is not permitted.

"Official drugs must be packaged and labeled as prescribed in the official texts. Unofficial drugs should be packaged so as to prevent deterioration."

When a prescription for a particular drug is filled with material that meets those rigid requirements, the physician can have every assurance that the integrity of his prescription has been preserved.

Drugs that fail to meet those requirements are illegal in interstate commerce. The experience of the Food and Drug Administration shows they are few.

The Why of Prescription Drugs

NEVIS E. COOK

Assistant to the Commissioner, Food and Drug Administration
Department of Health, Education, and Welfare
Washington, D. C.

In the debate that preceded passage of the Durham-Humphrey law, an amendment to the Federal Food, Drug, and Cosmetic Act that defines the types of drugs that must be restricted to prescription sale, there was quite general agreement that many of the modern drugs could be used with relative safety only under professional supervision. Much of the controversy over that amendment arose, not over its fundamental purpose, but over how that purpose could be accomplished without placing undue restrictions on the manufacturers, distributors, and users of drugs—particularly the professional people, pharmacists, and physicians.

It may well be said that the legal restrictions on the sale of certain drugs without prescription is a logical and necessary outgrowth of the golden age of medical discovery in which we live. A few decades ago, there were a relatively small number of drugs available that were likely to cause serious harm when used by the public for attempted self-medication. Aside from the narcotics (controlled under separate legislation), there were virtually no drugs in serious demand for nonmedical use.

The original Federal Food, Drug, and Cosmetic Act of 1938 proved reasonably effective in bringing about the removal of dangerous drugs from proprietary remedies promoted for direct sale to the public. This was accomplished under a provision of the Act that prohibited the distribution of a drug that could not safely be used in the manner recommended in its labeling. The original Act, however, did not deal forthrightly and specifically with the restriction of drugs to prescription sale. Attempts to accomplish that by regulations promulgated under the law were not altogether satisfactory, either to the administering agency or to those regulated.

The new-drug section of the 1938 law provided that a manufacturer could not distribute commercially any new drug until he had submitted to the Food and Drug Administration convincing evidence that it was safe to use in the manner recommended in its labeling. This provision would be virtually impossible to administer without an enforceable prescription restriction. The new-drug section must reach a determination that the usefulness of the drug outweighs its potentiality for harm before it can be released. Evidently it would be difficult to reach such a conclusion about many of the newer drugs if they could not be restricted to prescription sale but had to be released for indiscriminate use and promotion to the lay public.

Increasing misuse and abuse of the newer potent drugs led to the passage of the

Durham-Humphrey law. From our own experience before and since the passage of this law, in investigating the results of the misuse of drugs, we are convinced that this amendment is basically sound public health legislation and we believe it deserves the support of all in the health professions. When the measure was being considered by Congress, Dr. Walter P. Martin, testifying in behalf of the American Medical Association, gave the Association's endorsement to the majority of the objectives sought by the legislation, including those that were finally enacted into law. The bill also had the endorsement and has had the continuing support of the National Association of Retail Druggists.

Our correspondence indicates that there is some sentiment that the Food and Drug Administration arbitrarily restricts too many drugs to prescription sale. This criticism is balanced by other complaints that some drugs are released for over-the-counter sale without adequate evidence that they are safe for use in self-medication. The truth of the matter is that the administering agency has little room for arbitrariness in making decisions about what legally must be a prescription drug or an over-the-counter drug. We must operate within the framework of the law and Congress has established the public policy in this law that any drug that is safe enough to use for a condition that a layman can reasonably diagnose and treat must be labeled for sale without prescription. Conversely, it was the clear intent of Congress to restrict to prescription sale any drug that is, for whatever reason, not suitable for use in self-medication. In the last analysis it comes down to a question of the kind of testimony medical experts in the field involved can give about a particular drug. When some of the antihistaminic drugs were first released for sale without prescription, many of the physicians we consulted were dubious about whether it was in the public interest to release these drugs for use in self-medication; but, at the same time, they were unable to say that the drugs proposed for over-the-counter sale were not safe in the dosages recommended. The question of whether they were really useful in colds was so controversial that it would have been hopeless to try to litigate that issue. The burden of proof of ineffectiveness is upon the Government; the responsibility of showing safety is on the distributor.

Current medical literature bears adequate testimony to the need for restricting many of the modern drugs to prescription sale. Even when drugs are used with the greatest care by professional people, drug injuries are a major problem.

What Is a New Drug under the Food, Drug, and Cosmetic Act?

RALPH G. SMITH
Chief, New Drug Branch, Division of Medicine
Food and Drug Administration
U. S. Department of Health, Education, and Welfare
Washington, D. C.

The Federal Food, Drug, and Cosmetic Act of 1938 includes a section that, in effect, prohibits the introduction into interstate commerce of any new drug unless

an application for it is effective. The purpose of the application is to show that the drug is safe when used as recommended in its labeling. In spite of the fact that a distributor would usually satisfy himself that a drug was safe before marketing it, the preparation and processing of a formal application entails extra work, expense, and delay. Accordingly, this procedure is followed only when necessary, that is, when the product is a new drug. Consequently, the distributor is interested in knowing whether his drug falls within this classification.

A decision on the newness of a product is facilitated by the definition of a new drug in the Act. It is defined as one that is not generally recognized, among experts qualified by scientific training and experience to evaluate the safety of drugs, as safe for use under the conditions prescribed, recommended, or suggested in the labeling. According to this definition, it is lack of recognition of safety by experts that constitutes newness. Presumably the experts are those who are particularly qualified in their respective specialties or fields of medicine. Since a new drug is one that is not "generally" recognized as safe, such recognition by one or two experts would be insufficient to remove a drug from new drug status. Very important also is the concept that safety is considered from the standpoint of the proposed labeling or recommendations for use. Without labeling, an opinion on new drug status is essentially meaningless. There is, incidentally, an exception included in the definition that excludes drugs that were distributed under the same labeling representations prior to the effective date of the 1938 Act but that otherwise might be considered as "new" from the standpoint of lack of evidence of safety.

The definition of a new drug is extended by the stipulation that even though safety has been demonstrated by investigations to the extent that an application has been allowed to become effective permitting the marketing of the drug, it still is considered as a new drug until it has been used to a material extent and for a material time under the conditions provided for in the labeling. This serves as a further safeguard in that the drug must pass the test of safety under actual marketing conditions before ceasing to be a new drug. The maintenance of new drug status will naturally depend on a number of factors related to marketing experience, such as the volume of distribution, the incidence and importance of side effects or toxicity, and problems connected with the drug itself rather than with its action, such as adequate assay procedures, stability, and the ease with which a product of uniform properties can be manufactured.

The legal definition of a new drug is further amplified by a regulation that outlines various reasons or conditions that may cause a drug to be new. Not only the active ingredients of a product but also the so-called inactive ingredients, such as a menstruum, excipient, carrier, or coating, may cause it to be a new drug. In recent years, many new dispersing agents, preservatives, solvents, and stabilizers have become available for pharmaceutic use. We may, at times, be more concerned with such components than with active ingredients both from the standpoint of systemic effects and local reactions.

A combination of two or more old drugs may be a new drug, in view of the possibility of synergism, physical or chemical incompatibility, or the formation of a new compound by chemical interaction. A change in the proportion of ingredients of an old combination of drugs may cause it to be a new drug. A drug commonly recognized as safe for a certain medical use may become a new drug if offered for a new purpose, to produce a different action, or to affect another structure of the body. In most instances, if a drug is safe for one therapeutic purpose it is also safe in the same dosage for some other ailment. This, however, is not invariably true. Certain pathologic conditions may modify the metabolism of a drug, its concentration in the body, and, accordingly, the response of tissues to its action. Newness of a drug may also arise from an increase in dosage, a new route of administration, or an extension in the duration of therapy, since any of these changes may pose a question of safety.

If a product contains an ingredient that is a new chemical compound or even an old chemical compound that previously has not been used therapeutically, there can be little doubt that it is a new drug. On the other hand, there will always be borderline cases even when considered from the standpoint of the definition in the Act and the regulation. This is particularly true, since the reasons for newness outlined in the regulation are not obligatory but are only probable causes of newness necessitating a degree of judgment and interpretation.

A tentative decision as to whether a product is a new drug may be made either by the manufacturer or the Food and Drug Administration. In actual practice, we in the Administration are frequently consulted. In offering an opinion, we try to be as judicious and consistent as possible under the guidance of the law and regulation.

What Happens When a Drug Becomes Old,
Obsolete, or Dangerous

BERT J. VOS

Assistant Chief, Division of Pharmacology, Food and Drug Administration
Department of Health, Education, and Welfare
Washington, D. C.

Drugs are engaged in a constant struggle for survival not very different from the one taking place in the world of nature. With the passing years, any one of several fates may overtake a drug. In rare instances nothing at all seems to happen, and the drug may be said to have grown old gracefully. Such is the case with ether, which was introduced for anesthesia more than a hundred years ago and yet continues today as the most widely used general anesthetic agent. Clearly age is no handicap to those products that are fortunate enough to fill a real need.

In contrast to this are those drugs that become obsolete and sink quietly into well-deserved oblivion. In most instances, the process is so gradual that we are hardly aware of it. The new miracle drugs receive publicity as they come in, but the ones they replace get no headlines on the way out. One has to look into old treatises on materia medica to gain a picture of the great number of drugs which have fallen by the wayside. It is not just a question of naïve folk remedies but of drugs that enjoyed the dignity of being listed in the official compendia. Asafetida, for example, was used for such conditions as hysteria, colic, constipation, bronchitis, whooping cough, and asthma. It was still included in the eleventh revision of the *United States Pharmacopeia*, which was official until 1942, but few of the current textbooks of pharmacology now consider it even worthy of mention. It is perhaps typical of these obsolete drugs that while they were worthless, or nearly so, there was at the time no better remedy for the conditions in which they were used. It has been the policy of the Food and Drug Administration to allow this process of evolution in drug products to follow its natural course, as long as the claims made for a drug are not inconsistent with scientific knowledge. Asafetida may have some value as a carminative, and there is no objection to offering it for this purpose. However, if it were sold today for the cure of whooping cough, this would be considered a violation of the law.

Sometimes there is even danger that a drug will become obsolete prematurely. Some 25 years ago, the use of watery extracts of ergot in obstetrics was held up as an example of the blind continuation of a thoroughly irrational practice. It was well-known that none of the ergot alkaloids was sufficiently water soluble to impart significant activity to such preparations. That is, it was well-known until the dogged persistence of the obstetricians in their "error" led to a re-examination of the problem and the discovery of ergonovine, the alkaloid with sufficient water solubility to account for the activity in the extracts. As the advantages of pure preparations of this new alkaloid became apparent, the watery extracts fell once more into disuse because of their poor stability.

Drugs can become dangerous in a variety of ways. Occasionally the incidence of adverse reactions is so low that many years pass before the causal relation is established. Actually the drug was dangerous all along, and it is only the awareness that is new. Aminopyrine enjoyed a tremendous popularity before it was discovered to be the cause of occasional cases of agranulocytosis. Now its sale is restricted to prescription so that the physician can weigh this risk against the needs of the patient. In the case of dinitrophenol for the treatment of obesity, the sequence of events was compressed into a much shorter time, but the limitations of the Federal Food and Drugs Act then in effect were such that it had no jurisdiction over such a product, dangerous though it was. All the Food and Drug Administration could do was to warn the public that the compound was dangerous.

With the passage of the Federal Food, Drug, and Cosmetic Act in 1938, it became necessary to show that a drug was safe before it was put on the market. This has eliminated episodes such as the one in which more than 100 people lost their lives because diethylene glycol was used as a solvent for sulfanilamide without adequate investigation of its toxicity. When a dangerous drug appears on the market today, it is usually a consequence of a breakdown in the control procedures. An offending drug may be nonsterile, pyrogenic, of incorrect strength, or even labeled with the wrong name. As soon as the error is discovered, the producer is usually eager to recall the material from the market. If not, the Food and Drug Administration has the product seized, and by adequate publicity warns the physicians and, if necessary, the public in the area where the dangerous material has been distributed.

The Pharmaceutical Chemist and
Law Enforcement

FRANK H. WILEY

Chief, Division of Pharmaceutical Chemistry
Food and Drug Administration
Department of Health, Education, and Welfare
Washington, D. C.

The 18 years that have passed since the enactment of the Food, Drug, and Cosmetic Act of 1938 have witnessed an almost complete revision of drugs in common usage. The drugs that were considered indispensable in 1938 now constitute only a small proportion of the physician's armamentarium. A host of synthetic chemicals having specific physiologic actions are available for the cure and control of many diseases. Crude vegetable drugs are giving way to the use of their purified active components, and the development of antibiotics has provided the physician with a new means of combating those diseases that are of bacterial origin.

This change from the old complex elixirs, extracts, and tinctures to drugs containing the active medicinals in a relatively pure form has simplified many of the problems of the drug analyst. In addition, new analytic tools have been developed that have increased the precision of his examinations and permit a far more complete analysis of the material at hand.

The rate of improvement in analytic techniques has equaled, or perhaps exceeded, the rate of development of new pharmaceuticals. The old photometers of the 1930's that depended upon relatively nonselective filters to obtain the wave length of light desired have given way to the far more selective prism-type instruments. The range of these instruments has been expanded beyond the visual spectrum to include the ultraviolet and infrared regions. Absorption spectra measurements now provide accurate means of measuring the quantity of material present and also provide the means for its qualitative identification. The separatory funnels and complicated extractors have been replaced by chromatographic columns and countercurrent extractors for the separation of mixtures of closely related chemicals. With these techniques, the chemist may now in a matter of minutes make separations that he would not have attempted 10 years ago. Paper chromatography has proved an invaluable tool for the separation and identification of minute amounts of the components of a mixture and, in some instances, has yielded quantitative results. Even the old patriarch of analytic techniques, acid-base titration, has been rejuvenated through the development of titrimeters for the more accurate detection of the end point of the reaction and the use of nonaqueous media for titration.

Many of the newer therapeutic agents are very potent and the difference between the therapeutic and toxic doses may be quite small. When this is the case, much more rigid control must be exercised in the production of the finished product. Thus, the analytic procedure that serves as a basis for the control must be highly specific and reliable.

In the heyday of unrefined elixirs, fluid extract, and tinctures, it was not at all unusual for two chemists applying identical procedures to a material to arrive at divergent answers. Consequently, many of the regulatory proceedings were based solely upon the accuracy of declarations of composition on the label of the products. Judges and juries, without the advantage of scientific training, were placed in the unhappy position of deciding a highly technical dispute between two opposing groups of scientists.

As the drugs in common use became more highly refined and less complex in composition, the number of disagreements as to composition decreased. More and more of the litigations in the drug field are based on the efficacy of the preparations in the conditions for which it had been recommended. This trend may not have materially improved the situation for the judges and juries that must make the final decision, but it has largely removed the regulatory chemist from the role of a disputant to that of a witness to certain facts that form a basis for the opinions of the experts on therapy. We still encounter products whose compositions are not accurately stated on their labels. These may be the results of inadvertent errors in formulation or of faulty control practices. Few of these cases result in litigation, since the analysts can usually agree on the exact composition. As our techniques improve, fewer disagreements on analytic findings will need to be resolved by the courts.

Thus, the regulatory drug analyst finds that his services as a witness are required less frequently, and he has more time to devote to the detection of errors in compounding. The research chemist, who served as an expert in substantiating the accuracy of the methods employed by the analyst, similarly finds less demand for these services and has more time to devote to the development of improved analytic procedures.

It is stimulating to note the freedom with which technical information flows between the scientists in regulatory agencies and the regulated pharmaceutical industries. It is quite common to find these men freely collaborating in the solution of a common problem. This does not mean that industry has gained domination of the agency impowered with its regulation, nor does it indicate that industry has relinquished control of the manufacture of pharmaceuticals to the Government. It does indicate that scientists, in organizations that were once thought to be in opposition, have decided that through cooperation and collaboration they can better reach the common goal, the production of better therapeutic aids for the benefit of mankind.

A foreign visitor to the laboratory recently expressed some confusion when attending a conference in which personnel from regulatory agencies, representatives of pharmaceutical manufacturers, and members of the groups that develop standards for pharmaceuticals discussed freely their mutual problems and made plans for obtaining solutions of them. His amazement that such a conference was possible indicates that it is not a universal practice. After he had become convinced of the feasibility of such a conference, he observed that here might be one of the reasons for the leadership of the United States in the development and production of fine pharmaceuticals.

Over-the-counter Sales and the Pharmacist

NEVIS E. COOK

Assistant to the Commissioner
Food and Drug Administration
Department of Health, Education, and Welfare
Washington, D. C.

"Rx" and "OTC" are relatively recent terms added to the everyday vocabulary of the pharmacist and are becoming increasingly familiar to physicians as denoting, respectively, drugs restricted to prescription sale and drugs that may be sold "over-the-counter" without prescription.

An amendment to the Federal Food, Drug, and Cosmetic Act that became effective in 1952 contains definitions of drugs that must be restricted to prescription sale. These must be labeled "Caution: Federal law prohibits dispensing without prescription." Prescriptions for these drugs may not be refilled except as authorized by the prescribing physician.

In recognition of modern practices, the law provides that either the original prescription or the refill authorization may be given by telephone; it must be "reduced promptly to writing and filed by the pharmacist."

Two facts about this law deserve special comment. One is that the Food and Drug Administration has no arbitrary authority to decide which drugs must be restricted to prescription sale. The law provides definitions, and it is the initial responsibility of the manufacturer to determine the status of the product he distributes. The Administration will, of course, offer an opinion when given the facts. If a disagreement arises, the prescription or nonprescription status of a particular drug can be finally determined only by litigating the issue in a Federal court—not always the best forum for settling a medical question.

The second point that needs emphasis is that toxicity per se is not the only criterion for determining whether a drug should be restricted to prescription sale. It was the clear intent of Congress to restrict to prescription sale any drug that has no rational use in self-medication. For example, it would be difficult to classify the potent antibiotics as prescription drugs solely on the basis of inherent toxicity, but few would argue that they are not logically prescription drugs, because of potentialities for harmful effect apart from toxicity per se and also because of the serious nature of the conditions for which they are used.

Violations involving the illegal sale of prescription drugs fall into two principal categories. One is the sale of drugs for use in self-medication. The other is the sale of drugs for nonmedical use, primarily barbiturates and amphetamines or amphetamine-like drugs.

The Durham-Humphrey amendment has proved reasonably effective in the control of the first type of violation, the sale of prescription drugs for self-treatment of disease. This is in large measure due to the fact that sale of this type of drug is confined almost exclusively to the drugstore, and the vast majority of pharmacists are law-abiding, ethical professional people.

The illegal distribution of drugs like the barbiturates and amphetamines, in demand for nonmedical use, presents a more difficult problem. Here we increasingly have to deal with a bootleg type of operation, the drugs finding their way into bars, restaurants, truck stops, and other outlets wholly outside the normal chain of distribution of prescription drugs. In investigating such sales it is often difficult to determine just where the diversion from legitimate channels of trade took place or to prove interstate movement of the drugs—the latter, of course, a prerequisite to any action under the Federal law, since the interstate character of the operation must be shown to establish jurisdiction.

A committee of the House of Representatives is now considering the question of whether there should be additional Federal legislation to control drugs like the amphetamines and barbiturates.

How the Law Regulates Package Inserts and
the Labeling of Drugs

ROBERT S. ROE
Associate Commissioner of Food and Drugs
Department of Health, Education, and Welfare
Washington, D. C.

The original Food and Drugs Act of 1906 classed a drug as misbranded if its label failed to bear a statement of the quantity or proportion of any narcotic or of certain other substances, such as alcohol and acetanilid. In other respects the labeling requirements of the law were negative in character.

The law classed as misbranded any drug whose label bore any statement, design, or device regarding the article that was false or misleading in any particular. There was no requirement in the law for informative labeling beyond the disclosure of the presence of narcotics or the other designated drugs. It was believed, however, that the prohibition of false or misleading label statements included statements relative to the therapeutic efficacy of the products. This view was dispelled with the Supreme Court's decision in the Johnson case wherein it was held that the prohibition referred to false or misleading statements concerning the composition or identity of the product but did not encompass claims as to usefulness or therapeutic efficacy. Hence, the Dr. Johnson Cancer Cure was held not in violation of the law, since the representations and claims for cure, although false, did not contravene the statute.

The loophole in the law created by this decision was promptly eliminated with the enactment of the Sherley Amendment in 1912, which provided that a drug is misbranded "if its package or label shall bear or contain any statement, design, or device regarding the article or any of the ingredients or substances contained therein which is false and fraudulent." This amendment soon was challenged in a case that eventually went to the Supreme Court (Eckman's Alterative). The Court held that the amendment was constitutional and valid, and that the word "contain" was used in the amendment precisely to cover the matter of circulars or printed matter placed inside of the package. The defendant had challenged the application of the law to circulars contained in the cartons. Incidentally, statements in these circulars represented the product as an effective preventive for pneumonia and a cure for tuberculosis.

The amended Act of 1906 was not adequate to provide the consumer protection needed to deal with the newer modes of distribution and sales promotion in vogue by 1938. The requirement for establishing that a label claim was fraudulent as well as false was an insurmountable barrier to successful prosecution under many circumstances. The absence of informative labeling permitted the distribution of drug products without adequate directions to insure safe and efficacious use, and warnings against potential dangers.

The Food, Drug, and Cosmetic Act of 1938 provided for substantial and significant changes in the labeling requirements for drugs. The law distinguished between "label" and "labeling" and carefully defined labeling as all printed or written matter accompanying the article.

Those who persisted in selling their nostrums by means of misbranding claims resorted to circulars shipped separately from the article and frequently added to the package only after it had reached the dealers' shelves. When the Food and Drug Administration charged that literature so distributed constituted "accompanying labeling," a series of appellate court decisions resulted. For instance, in the Kordell case, the Supreme Court held that an article is "accompanied" by another when it supplements or explains it and that no physical attachments of one to the other is necessary, the textual relationship being significant. It was held that printed matter shipped separately and at different times from the drug but with a common origin and a common destination was in accompaniment with the drug. In 1948 the Supreme Court, in the Urbeteit case, held that leaflets shipped at different times from a therapeutic device "accompanied" the device. A circuit court of appeals, in the Color-Therm case, held that it is not necessary that instructions be physically attached to the devices to constitute labeling—that circulars typed in Oklahoma from copy sent from Kansas, and distributed by salesmen with the devices, constituted labeling.

Another subterfuge attempted repeatedly was to label the article in extremely simple terms, such as "Formula B—Take 1 teaspoon before meals," and then to make collateral claims that it would cure serious diseases. These claims were often made orally by pitchmen, "health experts" who organized lecture series, and by house-to-house salesmen. Others depended upon books or elaborate promotion schemes that would so fix the product and its so-called virtues in the minds of the public that claims on or in the package were unnecessary for sales. Regulations were issued defining "adequate directions for use" to include the requirement that directions should state all of the conditions, purposes, and uses for which the drug is intended, including those prescribed, recommended, or suggested in oral, written, printed, or graphic advertising. Appellate courts' decisions have in essence upheld the validity of this regulation.

The Act of 1938 has many positive requirements for informative labeling. It requires that the label or labeling contain adequate directions for use and adequate warnings against unsafe use by children or unsafe dosages and methods of administration. Other information required to appear on the label includes the name and address of the manufacturer or distributor, an accurate statement of quantity of contents, the common or usual name of the drug, and, if it is composed of two or more ingredients, the common or usual name of each active ingredient. Certain substances named in the law, such as alcohol, bromides, and acetanilid, whether active or not, must be declared quantitatively. Certain designated narcotic or hypnotic substances, such as narcotic alkaloids and barbituric acid and derivatives, must be declared quantitatively and the label must bear the statement "Warning—may be habit-forming." The Act also classes as misbranded any drug or device "if its labeling is false or misleading in any particular."

It is not the intent of the law to prohibit self-medication, rather it is obviously the purpose of the law to require that the information and the warnings in the labeling of drugs and devices will, insofar as practicable, enable their safe and efficacious use. There are certain classes of drugs that are restricted to distribution on prescription. These are drugs for which adequate directions for use cannot be prepared which will enable the safe and efficacious employment by the lay person. They include the habit-forming drugs and those drugs which are deemed unsafe except under the supervision of a licensed practitioner because of their toxicity or other potentiality for harm, or because of the collateral measures necessary for their use. They also include certain new drugs which have been restricted for use under professional supervision.

The Control of Imports under the Federal Food, Drug, and Cosmetic Act

J. KENNETH KIRK
Assistant to the Commissioner, Food and Drug Administration
Washington, D. C.

The terms of the Federal Food, Drug, and Cosmetic Act apply to imports of foods, drugs, devices, and cosmetics just as they do in the case of domestic interstate shipments of those items. The law, however, provides for a cooperative endeavor between the Secretary of the Treasury and the Secretary of Health, Education, and Welfare in the handling of goods offered for importation.

As this works out in practice, the Bureau of Customs of the Treasury Department notifies the Food and Drug Administration of any shipments of products subject to the Federal Food, Drug, and Cosmetic Act that are being offered for entry. The latter then decides whether to (1) collect samples from the importation, or (2) release the shipment without examination. In some cases, the decision may be aided by looking at the few packages brought to the Appraiser's Stores for customs purposes.

With its limited facilities, the Food and Drug Administration cannot examine samples from every shipment. In determining which shipments to sample, consideration is given to past experience on shipments of the product from the same shipper, the likelihood of encountering a violation, and general information about a specific industry or product. For example, during 1954, large importations of shelled peanuts were offered for entry from several countries. It was found that the importations from certain countries were uniformly infested with insects, so every shipment from those countries had to be sampled and examined. Peanuts from other sources were found uniformly satisfactory, however, so that only occasional shipments were sampled, the remainder being released without examination.

The Food and Drug District office notifies the Collector of Customs whether samples are desired from the lot. If they are, the Food and Drug inspectors usually collect the samples in cities where Food and Drug laboratories exist, whereas the Customs inspectors submit these samples from other points. Coincidentally, the importer is notified that the sample has been collected. By filing a redelivery bond with Customs, the importer may remove the goods from the transportation company dock. He is, however, required to hold the goods intact until they are released, either by notification that no samples are desired, or by formal notice after the collection and examination of samples. If he fails to do so, the bond may be forfeited.

If the Food and Drug Administration concludes that the product should be permitted entry, both the importer and the Collector of Customs are so notified. Occasionally, this notice will carry a comment about some minor violation that was encountered so that the importer will arrange for future shipments to be in complete compliance.

If it appears from the examination of the samples, or otherwise, that the product is in violation of the terms of the Federal Food, Drug, and Cosmetic Act, the Food and Drug District office issues to the importer a notice that the shipment is detained. Opportunity is given to the importer to appear at an informal hearing at the Food and Drug District office to offer any testimony that he may have tending to show that the proposed action involving the lot is in error. He may submit his views by letter if desired. This hearing may be continued, on reasonable grounds, in order to give the importer an opportunity to conduct his own examination of samples from the shipment, or, in some cases, to obtain information from the foreign shipper.

The importer has an opportunity to appeal an adverse decision to the Washington headquarters of the Food and Drug Administration, or, as is often the case, he may propose that the goods be released to him under bond to permit him to bring them into compliance with the law under the supervision of the Food and Drug Administration, by relabeling, cleaning, or other appropriate means. He may also propose that the goods be denatured so that they are suitable for some technical use, but no longer subject to the Act. If one of the latter courses is chosen, the importer may be granted the opportunity to attempt this. He is required to pay all of the expenses of the Food and Drug Administration and of the Bureau of Customs for supervising the operation, and normally must destroy any rejects from cleaning or segregating operations. If the reconditioning attempt is unsuccessful or if the importer does not request permission to bring the goods into compliance, a Notice of Refusal of Admission is issued. This notice requires the importer to export or destroy the goods under supervision of the Bureau of Customs within 90 days.

If the importer or owner of the goods believes that there is no sound basis for the refusal of admission, he can file a petition for injunction in Federal District Court. The Court will then hear the evidence with a view to determining whether the action taken in the case by the Government is to be classed as arbitrary, capricious, or unreasonable.

The Food and Drug Administration does not examine samples submitted to it by private parties who propose to ship goods to this country but is always willing to discuss proposals informally upon request and to offer any comment in the light of the requirements of the law. In order to do this, it is necessary that full information about the composition of the product and its proposed labeling be submitted by the inquirer. The Food and Drug Administration never announces which products are likely to be sampled at the time of importation over a given period. Similarly, the fact that an import shipment may be released at the time of entry cannot be taken as a guarantee that the product is in complete compliance with the law, since many shipments are released without examination and others may be examined to a limited extent. Imported products, found to be in violation of the law after release, may be recalled by the Bureau of Customs for reconsideration under import procedure. If they are not returned to the custody of the Bureau of Customs, they may be removed from the market under the seizure provisions of the Federal Food, Drug, and Cosmetic Act. This is accomplished by the filing of a libel against the goods in Federal District Court. The libel asks for condemnation of the lot. Such an action is subject to the same procedures as are all domestic seizures under the Act. Thus, there is a double check on some imported merchandise, in that it is subject to examination at the time of entry and also may be given attention as Food and Drug inspectors encounter the lots in warehouses or other establishments throughout the United States.

A Practicing Attorney Looks at the 1938 Federal
Food, Drug, and Cosmetic Act and Its Administration

CHARLES WESLEY DUNN

New York Bar
President of The Food Law Institute *
New York, N. Y.

A lawyer should first approach this Act from the viewpoint that it is a great public law of profound social and economic importance to our country. The Act governs our most essential food and drug industries and regulates our most essential food and drug products, and it does so for the essential purpose of protecting the public health by prohibiting an injurious adulteration or misbranding of its products.

---

* The Institute was established by leading food manufacturers to provide a better knowledge of the food and drug law by university instruction and basic research.

Hence it is a basic public health law. But it is more than that, for it is also a basic agricultural law by reason of its application to agricultural foods. For example, it establishes standards for their purity and controls their pesticide contamination. It is further a basic nutrition law to improve the national diet. Thus, among other things, it establishes standards for needed enriched foods, and it safeguards dietary foods. In addition, it is a basic pharmacy and medical law, to assure the safety, purity, and efficacy of necessary drugs and medicines.

A lawyer should next approach this Act from the viewpoint that it likewise has a profound legal importance, in itself, for two historic reasons. The first reason is that the predecessor of this Act, the original 1906 Federal Food and Drugs Act, was the third major law enacted by Congress to regulate interstate commerce at all. The other two laws were the 1887 Interstate Commerce Commission Act, to prevent discriminatory charges by railroads, and the 1890 Sherman Antitrust Act, to suppress wrongful private monopoly. The second reason is that the present 1938 Act uses a regulation of interstate commerce to regulate intrastate commerce as well. For it jurisdictionally reaches all intrastate commerce in its products, where they originated in interstate commerce; and all intrastate commerce in oleomargarine, even if it never entered interstate commerce, which is a significant extension of the Federal Government to control local affairs also.

For these reasons, the legal profession must give the Act before us a high place in our socioeconomic history and in our national jurisprudence, a statement emphasized by the following practical fact: The law of this Act and its predecessor has been the legal basis for the incredible renaissance of our food and drug industries in the first half of the twentieth century. It has freed them from the restraint of destructive product competition; it has thus released their creative genius for beneficial exercise in our dynamic free enterprise system; and it has thus permitted them to make constructive use of their infinite scientific and technologic resources. As a result they have made greater progress in food and drug improvement in the last 50 years than ever before, and they have provided our people with the highest food and drug standards yet achieved. Hence it is most fitting that we commemorate the fiftieth anniversary of this public law in 1956, which is the one of greatest importance to the largest number of our people, to wit, the consuming public.

Moreover, the legal profession should also recognize that this Act has been superbly administered by the Food and Drug Administration, as a rule. This I know from my own professional experience with its administration, for more than 40 years. The FDA is an expert and career professional agency of the Federal Government, specially organized to administer this Act; it is directed by able executives and competent scientists; and it is manned by dedicated public servants. The FDA has the tremendous responsibility of protecting every man, woman, and child in this country from death or injury by the adulteration or misbranding of food and drugs, and it has successfully met this responsibility, notwithstanding the handicap of inadequate appropriations. But fortunately that situation is in process of repair through the corrective report last year by the Citizens Advisory Committee, which is now beginning to receive due implementation by Congress.

The Food and Drug Administration
Prepares a Case for Court

JOSEPH L. MAGUIRE

Assistant Chief, Food and Drug Division
Office of the General Counsel
Department of Health, Education, and Welfare
Washington, D. C.

An important aspect of the varied functions of the Food and Drug Administration, Department of Health, Education, and Welfare, is the enforcement of the provisions of the Federal Food, Drug, and Cosmetic Act. Enacted in 1938, it has been amended in several important respects.

The Administration recommendations for enforcement are sent to the Department of Justice, either to the Attorney General, or, upon his authority, directly to a United States attorney. The cases are of three types: seizures of interstate shipments of adulterated or misbranded food, drugs, devices, or cosmetics; prosecutions for violations of the Act; and injunctions to prevent prospective criminal violations.

The operating procedures adopted by the Administration for its several divisions are geared to mesh smoothly when it becomes known that a trial impends. Apart from the issuance of supervisory orders that initiate an investigation, the first steps taken along the route to a court contest are usually by Administration inspectors. Their educational qualifications are high. Most are college graduates who have majored in a science, such as chemistry, biology, or pharmacy. Their training and instructions, while apprenticing, are directed to the execution of the minutiae of each assignment with such a degree of attention to detail that the work product, if subjected to judicial scrutiny, would not be found wanting. Standard forms that they use for documenting the collection of samples and for notices of factory inspection and the requirements for the reports of their investigations have all been planned with the objective of possible use for or at trial.

The collected sample, meticulously documented, identified, and sealed, is transmitted and assigned to an analyst at one of the district laboratories. If highly specialized equipment, training, experience, or knowledge is required, which is not available in the field, the sample is sent to the Washington headquarters and there assigned for special attention.

The labeling, work sheets, and reports of the analysts are reviewed by the chief of the division or supervisory officials in the several districts. If it appears that a violation of the Act has been committed, the alleged violative goods are available, and there is proof necessary to establish movement in interstate commerce, a recommendation to seize is made. All supporting data are forwarded to Washington for review, and, if the recommendation is concurred in, the matter is sent to the Food and Drug Division of the General Counsel's office. It is reviewed there before transmittal to the Department of Justice. Prior to the institution of criminal prosecution, the Act specifies the alleged violators be given an opportunity for a hearing. Disclosures at the hearing are considered in determining whether prosecution will be recommended. Except for the hearing, similar study, review, and checks are made before a case is sent to the Attorney General for injunction proceedings.

If the article in litigation is a device, an Administration physicist will enlist the aid of a professor in the chemistry, physics, or electronics department of a university to make tests or studies in addition to those made in the Administration laboratory. The prestige of such scholastic attainments, his nonpartisan academic interest in the problems entailed, and the reputation of the institution with which the professor is affiliated lend prestige to the Government presentation. A court and jury can scarcely fail to be impressed when a Geiger counter, used in a courtroom test by the professor, remains ominously undisturbed by a gadget claimed to cure the gamut of human ills from warts, hiccoughs, and dandruff to diabetes and cancer by means of radioactive emanations.

In a drug or device case where unwarranted claims for therapeutic effects are made, a physician member of the division of medicine may solicit the assistance of an outstanding clinic or university hospital in order to take advantage of the advanced procedures, thinking, and knowledge that prevail there. Such aid is invariably granted. Testimony of clinical studies proving the worthlessness of the claims for the medicament are disclosed in court.

The help of individual physicians who are highly qualified in their respective specialties and who usually practice in the locale of the court's jurisdiction is frequently sought and readily granted. These practitioners, where the prevailing circumstances are appropriate, will conduct examinations and tests using authenticated material furnished by the Administration. Their expert opinions based on the results they have observed and the facts they have found are presented in support of the Government's charges.

Associations of product processors, distributors, and affiliated organizations extend their cooperation by furnishing information and, on occasion, testimony to support the Government charges of adulteration or misbranding perpetrated by an unscrupulous operator.

In cases where a product, after shipment in interstate commerce, has become violative, by reason of the misdeed of another, shippers willingly furnish the testimony to show the article was legitimate when shipped. Many of these instances have occurred in the last few years in trials involving the improper sale, at retail level, of prescription drugs.

The case as it is presented at trial reflects the coordination of the various divisions of the Food and Drug Administration with able assists from cooperating clinics, institutions, physicians, other professional personnel, associations, legitimate industry, and many others solicitous of protecting the public.

Administration appropriations, it is well known, are low. Personnel is thereby sharply limited and investigational surveillance curtailed. It is an encomium for the vast majority of persons and firms engaged in supplying the American public with the vital and essential items covered by the Act, estimated at approximately $65 billion per annum, that but a minute number of the shipments made are of violative products for which enforcement actions are instituted. It is a tribute, too, to the scrutiny and good judgment of the Administration that but few cases it submits for litigation are contested. Of the latter, a minimal number have terminated unsuccessfully over the years.

The Food and Drug Witness in Court

GILBERT S. GOLDHAMMER
Assistant Director, Regulatory Management, Food and Drug Administration
Department of Health, Education, and Welfare
Washington, D. C.

The Food, Drug, and Cosmetic Act was enacted by Congress as an instrument for consumer protection. It provides for the seizure and removal from channels of interstate commerce of misbranded and adulterated foods, drugs, therapeutic or diagnostic devices, and cosmetics. It also provides for injunction to restrain violations and for criminal prosecution of violators. All three sanctions—seizure, injunction, and prosecution—are sought only in a Federal court of law by the Department of Justice upon the filing of an appropriate complaint or charge with the United States District Court by the United States Attorney.

In a seizure, the complaint is known as a libel, and in criminal prosecutions, it is known as an information, or if it is returned by a Grand Jury, an indictment. All libels, informations, indictments, and complaints for injunction have one thing in common; they all allege that a specific article of food, drug, device, or cosmetic is adulterated or misbranded, or both, within the meaning of the Federal Food, Drug, and Cosmetic Act. Other allegations in the complaints normally relate to interstate shipments, labeling of the articles, and the persons making and receiving the interstate shipments.

The owner of an article seized may appear in court as claimant and may ask permission of the court to legalize the products, or he may deny the allegations of the libel. In criminal prosecution, the defendant may deny the allegations of the information or indictment by a plea of "not guilty." Likewise in injunction suits, the defendant may deny the Government's charges.

When such denials are made, a trial in court before a judge or jury results. Naturally, trials are serious matters, for there is usually much at stake for both sides.

Court trials are won by evidence, and since the witness is generally the medium through which evidence is introduced, the Food and Drug Administration, like other law enforcing agencies, considers the witness of primary importance. The success of the Food and Drug Administration's work in public protection, especially when the outcome of a trial profoundly affects an enforcement program, often hinges upon the persuasiveness of its witnesses during the trial.

In almost all Food and Drug trials, whether they be concerned with a fake cancer cure, nonsterility of sutures, a deficiency of potency in an antibiotic, filth in food, the watering of oysters, or the substitution of peanut oil for olive oil, the scientist or expert holds the key to success for the Government. Vigorously contested trials often develop into a battle of the experts. Fortunately, the Government has been singularly successful in such battles, and the way lay juries and judges discern the truth in such scientific and technical disputes is a tribute to our judicial system. The Government has usually been able to present as its experts men who are among the foremost in their fields. These experts not only know their subject matter but they are also skillful in giving their testimony in lay terms a judge and jury can comprehend. The Government also has been fortunate in obtaining witnesses recognized as authorities in the community where the trial is held.

The expert medical or scientific witness is only one of many who may appear in the trial of a Food and Drug case. The areas of human endeavor covered by the Food, Drug, and Cosmetic Act are so broad that great variety exists in the kinds of cases brought and witnesses required. Truckers, truck drivers, wholesalers, or retailers may be required to prove interstate shipment. To prove adulteration or misbranding, Food and Drug inspectors, chemists, microbiologists, microanalysts, entomologists, pharmacologists, physicists, hospital librarians, sanitarians, and pharmacists may be called. To establish the misleading character of labeling statements, testimony of consumers, psychologists, public opinion experts, and marketing and advertising specialists may be presented. Members of the trade may be employed to testify about trade practices and standards when such testimony is necessary to establish violations that could have been avoided and are not condoned by fellow producers.

Witnesses generally realize their importance to the work of the Food and Drug Administration and freely offer their cooperation. This is especially so with the expert—the physician, pathologist, pharmacologist, or other scientist—who is called upon to testify for the Government.

It is always a sacrifice for a physician to leave his busy practice or a scientist to leave his work to spend an indeterminate amount of time in testifying or waiting in the courtroom for his turn. The small fee the Government is able to pay expert witnesses in comparison with private concerns does not put it in a bargaining position or even in a hiring one. It is most gratifying to note the high caliber of the men who respond to the Food and Drug Administration's call for assistance. It reflects an unusual recognition of responsibility to the public welfare. Their reward in testifying rests in the personal satisfaction derived from a real contribution toward the protection of public health or the elimination of quackery or fraud.

The Role of the Food and Drug Administration in the Control of Drug Addiction

H. G. UNDERWOOD

Assistant Director, Division of Program Planning
Food and Drug Administration, Department of Health, Education, and Welfare
Washington, D. C.

Congressional hearings by the House Subcommittee on Narcotics in 1951 and 1955, by the Senate Subcommittee to Investigate Juvenile Delinquency in 1953 and 1954, and by the Senate Subcommittee on Narcotics in 1955 focused attention on the extent to which the Federal Food, Drug, and Cosmetic Act can and is being applied to control traffic in two classes of drugs capable of causing addiction that are not controlled under the narcotics laws administered by the Bureau of Narcotics. The classes considered, the barbiturates and amphetamines, are valuable drugs when properly used under medical supervision. While there is controversy whether these classes of drugs are truly addicting, there is no dispute that they have been subject to serious misuse.

Because the Act makes no special provision for control of the distribution of barbiturates and amphetamines, the enforcement activities against their illicit distribution are linked with those against the illegal sale of antibiotics, abortifacients, hormones, sulfonamides, and other dangerous drugs.

The most important section of the Act to prevent misuse of drugs is the amendment of Section 503 (b), popularly known as the Durham-Humphrey Amendment, which became effective in April, 1952. Up to that time the control exercised under the Act was under the general terms of the statute and implementing regulations.

The initial effort to regulate traffic in dangerous drugs was educational. Druggists and others were made aware of the requirements of the Act by publicity in the trade press, through special bulletins issued by professional associations, and through the cooperation of the Boards of Pharmacy and other State and local officials. Notwithstanding the extensive educational activity, dangerous drugs continued to reach the public without prescription. The Administration then began to develop cases to support the educational program. Congress passed the Durham-Humphrey Amendment to define clearly the pharmacist's obligations in the dispensing of dangerous drugs.

The amendment divides all drugs into two classes: (1) those too dangerous for lay use, and (2) those for which adequate directions can be written for the layman. The dangerous drugs must bear the statement "Caution: Federal law prohibits dispensing without prescription." To avoid confusion, the amendment makes it unlawful to put the legend on a drug that is suitable for self-medication. The amendment makes it a violation to dispense prescription-legend drugs except on the prescription of a practitioner licensed by law to administer such drugs or to refill such a prescription without authorization of the prescriber.

Because misuse of barbiturates and amphetamines may result in serious antisocial problems, special effort has been made to locate and correct abuses. The Administration receives leads from pharmacists, hospitals, medical associations, police departments, and others. The Administration often receives letters or visits from members of families about an addiction or misuse problem.

While the Act was not intended to regulate the professional acts of licensed practitioners, the Administration has named doctors as co-defendants with druggists in a few cases. Such cases involved doctors who, for a fee, wrote blank prescriptions that the druggist filled in as illegal sales were made or who signed prescriptions the druggist wrote for such sales. Recently the Administration filed a case against a physician who furnished barbiturates and amphetamines to inspectors under circumstances that confirmed reports that he was trafficking in such drugs other than on a bona fide doctor-patient relationship. The development of this type of case is difficult because of the extent of the evidence necessary to prove to a court that the physician's acts are not a part of his professional prerogatives.

Many States have passed special laws to control these and other dangerous drugs as the result of concern shown by ethical pharmacists, professional organizations, and State Boards of Pharmacy over the barbiturate and amphetamine problem. Despite these State laws, few, if any, States have enough inspectors for effective enforcement. Some States develop leads to violations and then request Federal assistance to help develop cases for presentation in Federal Court. State enforcement officials sometimes believe Federal Courts inflict more salutary penalties. Some States suspend the license of a drug store and its pharmacist after a conviction in Federal Court.

Enforcement under State laws may, in some instances, be less difficult than under the Federal law because under many State laws illegal possession of one or both classes of these drugs is an offense and State enforcement officials generally have ready access to prescription records. Also, State officials do not have to prove the drugs moved in interstate commerce. Illegal possession of these classes of drugs is not an offense under Federal law as is the case with narcotics. Although the Federal Act requires the pharmacist to keep a prescription record for dangerous drugs, one section denies Federal inspectors access to such files except on a voluntary basis.

In view of the limited manpower to enforce the Federal and State laws dealing with the illegal sale of dangerous drugs, the cooperative efforts of both the Federal and the State enforcement agencies is necessary to deal with this serious problem.

As barbiturates and amphetamines have become increasingly difficult to get in many drug stores, an underworld interest has sprung up. While a number of cases have been developed, chiefly involving non-drugstore outlets selling amphetamines to truck drivers, the Administration does not have the personnel to delve very deeply into this bootleg-type traffic and therefore it does not know the extent of this traffic.

While the combined educational activities of the pharmacists' organization and the trade press and the Federal, State, and local enforcement activities have produced a beneficial effect, the Administration continues to receive numerous reports of abuses. Of the 142 Federal cases terminated in fiscal year 1955 for illegal sale of dangerous drugs, 84 were based on complaints of illegal dispensing of barbiturates and amphetamines.

During recent years, the Administration has been able to utilize only about 25 man-years of inspection time in investigating the unauthorized sale of all dangerous drugs. The expansion in the Food and Drug Administration staff contemplated by the recent report of The Citizens' Advisory Committee on the Food and Drug Administration would permit more extensive regulation of illicit traffic in these dangerous drugs through enforcement, education, and the development of state cooperation.

Quackery and the Law

GORDON A. GRANGER
Division of Medicine, Food and Drug Administration
Department of Health, Education, and Welfare
Washington, D. C.

Quackery, as defined in the dictionary, refers to "charlatanry" as an alternate and well-applied term. It is further defined as a false claim to medical knowledge and treating the sick without knowledge of medicine or authority to practice. Those who have had intimate and prolonged experience in treating the sick learn that all parts of the dictionary definition apply.

It is always interesting to speculate upon the question, "Why a quack?" Only the quack himself may supply an accurate answer to this ever-present question, but it seems clear that there are three types of individuals engaging in quackery.

The first, and most vicious, is the individual who for money, and money alone, engages in the use and distribution of a preparation for the treatment and cure of human ills. He is the individual who has a callous disregard for the welfare of unfortunates who fall into his hands and is interested only in their money. The second type is the truly misguided and ignorant individual who is convinced he has a sure cure for certain ailments and will treat patients under any conditions or circumstances in order to demonstrate his great cure. It is true that this type of person is interested in monetary returns and may hope to make his living from it, but his basic drive appears to be to convince the world of the merit of his wonderful remedy. The third type is the individual who has been frustrated in his desire to become a true practitioner of the healing arts and, by sketchy reading, has tried to fit himself to treat the sick even if it be done illegally.

The types of quackery run the gamut of all human ills. The cancer field has been exploited for many years and is being exploited at this time. The widespread publicity given to this disease in recent years has been necessary and has served a great and beneficial purpose but, like so many splendid endeavors, has had its ill effects. It is unfortunate, but true, that the campaign to make the public cancer conscious and to get people to their physicians for periodic examinations has indirectly served the purpose of the purveyors of worthless cancer remedies.

The diabetic field has been exploited in every way possible by purveyors of fake diabetic remedies. Some of these remedies have been composed of weeds and herbs and some of simple chemicals. The first line of attack in the diabetic remedies is to advise and insist that the patient discontinue insulin. In addition, the patients are further advised to eat anything they wish, and one well-known quack advised that large quantities of honey be eaten daily.

The food faddists, the arthritis experts, and the weight-reducing experts are all hard at work today. The rejuvenation experts had their day and had faded out of the picture prior to the development of testosterone. With the advent of that valuable drug, they returned in full force, but, fortunately, the resurgence was nipped in the bud.

How do the quacks operate? There is no set *modus operandi*, since each of the "specialists" has his own tried and true technique. Some operate behind the front of licensed practitioners. Some are licensed to practice the healing arts, and under the cover of their license, practice the crudest forms of quackery. Others operate as "lecturers," giving a series of well-advertised lectures in city after city. These lectures are ostensibly on health subjects, but the lecturer usually has a display at hand of whatever remedy or remedies he may be peddling at the time and the remedies fit neatly into his lecture. Some operate from town to town, setting up business in a hotel room and, by word of mouth, their presence and their specialty is made known. This type is usually "on the run," and is most often successful in leaving town just ahead of local authorities. The least troublesome, but dangerous nevertheless, is the individual, and usually an elderly resident of a locality, who has set himself up as an authority and will attempt to treat anyone who may come to him. This quack may or may not use drugs, but his usual armamentarium is a group of remedies he claims have been handed down in his family from generation to generation and that he alone may concoct. He may or may not charge a fee, but he is always very grateful for any donations offered.

Can the practicing physician be of assistance in this battle against quackery and the needless squandering of human lives? He can and he must! First, what information can a physician give his patients so that they may be able to detect a quack? The remedy is always a secret one, discovered by the quack, and only he knows how to use it. He is persecuted by the "medical trust." The "medical trust" persecute him and deny his methods because they cannot afford financially to permit a real cure to be available. There is a direct or implied promise to cure and a direct and immediate attack on all recognized methods of treatment. They make adroit and powerful attacks on the medical profession and they attempt, too often successfully, to destroy the patients' confidence in their physicians and the methods employed by them. If the practicing physician can point out to his patients these outstanding earmarks of the quack, he will have taken one long step on the road to educating the public in evaluating the quack.

A cardinal point in this battle relates to the patient with cancer. Too many times the physician, at the termination of a course of treatment, has informed the family that he has done all he can do and the outcome is inevitable. Such a course, in too many instances, is tantamount to buying the patient a ticket to the nearest or most widely known cancer quack. The physician must keep this fact ever before him in his relations with these patients and in his handling of them and their family. If he can keep this very important fact in mind and continue his patient-physician relationship, he will have taken one more long step down the road to victory over the quacks and quackery.

The application of the Food, Drug, and Cosmetic Act to quackery is always difficult and sometimes impossible. The extent and types of quackery extant could not be contemplated at the time the present law was drawn and passed by the Congress. The Food and Drug Administration has made, and is making, every endeavor to apply present provisions of the Act to quackery as it exists today.

The Food, Drug, and Cosmetic Act, in a general way, cannot be applied until it can be proved that interstate commerce is involved. The law deals with labels, labeling, and the misbranding of drugs through labels and labeling. A drug is defined in the Act (in part), as an article intended for use in the diagnosis, cure, mitigation, treatment, or prevention of disease in man or other animals and, also as an article (other than food) intended to affect the structure or any function of the body of man or other animals.

The term "label" means a display of written, printed, or graphic matter upon the immediate container of any article. The term "labeling" means all labels and other written, printed, or graphic matter (1) upon any article or any of its containers or wrappers, or (2) accompanying such an article (in interstate commerce).

Under "Prohibited Acts," Food, Drug, and Cosmetic Act, are the following: "The following acts and the causing thereof are hereby prohibited: (1) the introduction or delivery for introduction into interstate commerce of any food, drug, device or cosmetic that is adulterated or misbranded."

The Federal courts have held that printed or graphic matter must not necessarily move in interstate commerce with a drug to constitute labeling if they come together at a common destination. The Federal courts have also held that oral representations for intended use may constitute labeling if the goods on sale have moved in interstate commerce. This latter point has been of great assistance in dealing with the "pitchman" type of quackery and the so-called health lecturer.

In the battle to overcome the quacks, it has been necessary to prove misbranding of the drugs they use and also that interstate commerce is involved. The quack need not personally ship the drug in interstate commerce, but, if he hands it to a patient going to another state, he has "delivered for introduction into interstate commerce."

In preparing a case against a quack, a number of points must be established: (1) that a drug as defined in the law is involved; (2) that interstate commerce is involved beyond a shadow of a doubt; (3) that labeling is in use and that it and the drug have come together at a common destination after moving in interstate commerce; (4) that the labeling serves to misbrand the drug by making false and misleading representations; and (5) when all of these data are obtained, the case must be presented before a Federal judge or a judge and jury.

To gather all of the material necessary to make a solid case that can stand up in court takes a tremendous amount of time and work by the administrative, inspectional, and medical staffs, each of which plays an important and integrated part in development of the necessary evidence. The quacks, however, are very helpful in many instances. They cannot exist and prosper in the manner to which they have become accustomed without the use of promotional material, such as booklets, leaflets, and testimonials. All of this material may, under the proper circumstances, be considered labeling that serves to misbrand the drug. When the evidence is considered to be sufficient to prove our case, it is submitted to the Department of Justice, which presents the case in court with the advice and assistance of the proper Food and Drug Administration officials.

The Food and Drug Administration has developed many successful legal cases against quacks of all types. Our endeavors have been hampered by a lack of funds, owing to budgetary restrictions, but we are continuing in the work with all of our available resources.

Economic Cheats and the Law

FRANK A. VORHES, JR.
Director, Division of Food
Food and Drug Administration
Washington, D. C.

In the crude old market game of "thumb on the scales," not often played any more, the contestants at least faced each other squarely. In retrospect, there seems almost a tinge of sportsmanship in the way the even then infrequent cheater accepted some risk of discovery, knowing full well that the observant buyer, alert to the philosophy of *caveat emptor*, was being afforded a chance to protect his own interests.

It is common observation these days that progress in commodity distribution has brought with it a minimization of those personal contacts and a gradual disappearance of those simpler mechanics of retail trade that formerly often provided the customer some opportunity to exercise his own resources in pursuit of his own money's worth. Moreover, these changes have clothed the purveyor in a kind of anonymity, and it is a remarkable characteristic of human behavior that people will tolerate imposition at the hands of a remote uncertain perpetrator, which they would not abide from an identifiable neighbor. Fortunately, and doubtless in enlightened recognition of what constitutes good business, there has been concurrent improvement in industrial and mercantile practice, having the effect of generating a consumer confidence well-merited by the great bulk of the nation's food and drug supply. Paradoxically, this favorable development presents the few remaining chiselers an enhanced opportunity, for it is manifestly basic to the practice of fraud that people can more readily be swindled if their trust be first secured.

The unscrupulous are aided also by the relative ease with which substitution and inferiority may be concealed from ordinary observation in today's processed, compounded, packaged foods. So, likewise, is it easy, in the aura of current nutritional and therapeutic progress, to capture general credulity for those exaggerated and baseless claims of benefit that the "gyp artist" will ascribe to common foods and impotent nostrums.

Lincoln once said something to the effect that good government exists to do for the citizen what he cannot do for himself. The Federal Food, Drug, and Cosmetic Act is an instrument of that kind of government. Among its provisions are those designed to protect the public from economic victimization by the relatively small segment of the food and drug industries that may be disposed to traffic in debased and misrepresented goods. Of no small related significance, to the bulk of those industries, is the salutary influence of these provisions of the act in mitigation of disruptive trade practice represented by the activity of this minor fraction of their fellow businessmen. For their comparative number is evidently few; yet, obviously, the share they can steal of this 50 billion dollar annual commerce could well be minute indeed, and still account for a huge amount of groceries and medicine.

In the first order of cheater-prevalence is, no doubt, the short-weighter. The adulterant he uses is that most commonly available—free air. But it's not so free in the guise and at the price of even the most inexpensive food.

Dilution is next in prominence, palming off tap water in lieu of part of the product. The fact that water is a normal component of most foods makes it often easy to add some more without ready detection.

Since these adulterants, air and water, cost nothing, the entire substitution is clear profit. Recognizing that profit in the food industry does not ordinarily exceed a small per cent of gross value of production, it is evident that proportionate profit increase consequent to comparatively minor weight shortage, or relatively small dilution, may become tempting indeed.

The up-graders march third in this parade of rascals. By false promise of higher than actual quality, they also get something more, for absolutely nothing.

There are other, more subtle and ingenious, types of cheat, too many here to record. But mention must be made of the meanest of all, the false claim of nutrient or therapeutic benefit. Good, cheap, wholesome food products, that are nothing more than that, are recurrently exploited as modern miracles. At exorbitant charges, common mixtures of vitamins and minerals, virtuous enough in their own limited right, are peddled as boons to mankind; and worthless nostrums are extolled as lifesavers, in the lowest form of misrepresentation. Conscienceless fakers ply their trade in such as these with all the trappings of last century's "medicine man." Their pitch is obviously directed to the weak and the ill, those most to be harmed by their vicious deception.

Obviously the individual citizen is not prepared to avoid the swindlers of these ilks. It therefore becomes the obligation of government to hold them in check through effective enforcement of provisions of law adequate to these ends.

Therapeutic Devices and the
Federal Food, Drug, and Cosmetic Act

GORDON A. GRANGER
Division of Medicine, Food and Drug Administration
Department of Health, Education, and Welfare
Washington, D.C.

The term "device" is defined in the Food, Drug, and Cosmetic Act as "instru⁻ ments, apparatus, and contrivances, including their components, parts, and accessories, intended (1) for use in the diagnosis, cure, mitigation, treatment, or prevention of disease in man or other animals; or (2) to affect the structure or any function of the body of man or other animals." This definition clearly and concisely differentiates the device from drugs or other therapeutic or diagnostic measures.

The original Act of 1906 did not contain a provision for dealing with devices of any description. As time wore on, and while the Act of 1938 was in the process of preparation, it became clear that there must be a means for properly labeling devices intended for legitimate distribution and for dealing with the device that the fraud and quack could distribute and use. Thus, the provisions of the 1938 Act defining devices were born.

When the Act of 1938 became effective in all of its provisions, it became obvious that a monumental job confronted the Administration in the appropriate labeling of devices. This problem involved not only the quack type of device but the legitimate devices, such as the roentgen-ray and diathermy machines used by physicians, clinics, and hospitals. The labeling provisions of the Act referred directly to devices in the same sense that it referred to drugs. In other words, both adulteration and misbranding provisions referred to drugs and devices. An extensive study revealed problems in the distribution and use of devices that did not exist in the drug field. These problems required that regulations be drafted differing sufficiently from the drug regulations to provide for the problems at hand. This knotty problem has been adequately resolved.

At the same time, the problem of the quack devices was demanding attention. There were no precedents for developing legal cases in this field and many problems were encountered that were new and different in all respects. Most devices encountered at the outset were of an electrical nature. We soon learned that many of these gadgets required a study of electrical circuits that could not be carried out in our laboratories. It was necessary to add a physicist to our staff in order to fulfill our obligations in enforcing the pertinent provisions of the Food, Drug, and Cosmetic Act.

The devices encountered were of every description. Many were of a diagnostic type, to be applied directly to the patient or to make a diagnosis at a distance, for example, from a sample of blood, handwriting, urine, or sputum. Others were operated in the office of a quack. It followed that the long-distance diagnosis could be hooked up to a long-distance treatment for the many and varied diseases resulting from the diagnosis. The treatment was administered only after the payment of an appropriate fee.

These devices were often bizarre in character. Some of the quacks who operated from an office setup preferred a device with a multitude of dials, switches, and meters, none of which was of significance. Others preferred devices that showed flashing lights, buzzers, or bells to indicate the location of diseased areas. All of these machines had to be evaluated on the basis of physical characteristics and qualities and coordinated with accepted scientific facts.

Some of the devices that proved to be most troublesome, from an enforcement standpoint, did not fall into the above categories. One of the outstanding examples of this type was known as the "Virillium Tube," or "The Magic Spike." It was alleged to contain a potent substance and was worn attached to the clothing at one or another location, and its magic emanations cured just about all human ills. After lengthy and bitterly contested legal battles, this device was laid away. Another extensively promoted device was known as the "Spectrochrome," developed and promoted by an East Indian named Dinshah P. Ghadiali. This was a metal housing for an ordinary electric bulb, with a water container for cooling purposes. Attached were a group of colored glass squares arranged in slides so the light could shine through any of the slides or a combination of them. A chart was provided, dividing the body into areas corresponding to the various colored glass slides. The sick user consulted the chart, found the proper area and color combination, sat in front of the projector, and proceeded to be "cured." This was all intertwined with semireligious mumbo jumbo, diet, and living regimen. A school had been developed in connection with the promotion; the chosen disciples were given a course of instruction and then went out to instruct others in the proper use of the machine. After lengthy legal battles, interstate shipments of this contraption were eventually ended, and heavy penalties were imposed upon the promoter. Unfortunately, organized groups are still attempting to perpetrate the racket within the borders of a number of states.

The quacks and racketeers are ever sensitive to the times and the developments of the day. It was inevitable that, in our atomic-conscious era, the quack and racketeer would take advantage of a situation tailor-made for them. And so was born the "Atomatrone"—a completely worthless gadget composed of a single radio tube hooked up to an ordinary piece of window screen. Why? No one knows the answer to that one, but it did have an impressive appearance. Incorporated was an ordinary ultraviolet electric bulb shining through a group of colored glass slides into two 1 gallon containers of water. The water was "irradiated" for a given period of time and then consumed in the treatment of every known disease including diabetes, "coronary disease," and cancer. Again, lengthy legal battles ensued before the distribution of these devices could be stopped.

Also in keeping with the times are the uranium caves, mines, and sand. Rooms and caves are lined with sacks of uranium ore and benches built for the "patients" to sit upon while receiving the benefits from emanations of the order of those of the luminous dial of a wrist watch. The financial consideration is based upon time of treatment, usually a certain sum per hour. This racket has aimed at arthritics.

It has been possible to end this racket where the Food and Drug Administration has been able to establish the fact that there was interstate shipment of the uranium ore or sand. The mines, if uranium mines they are, do not fall within the scope of our activities.

We are assured, however, on long experience, that the quacks and racketeers will always come up with a new one. As new developments in the world of science become publicized and the public becomes conscious of these developments, the promoters of these often bizarre devices will not miss the opportunity for another and perhaps greater payday.

The Orgone Energy Accumulator
Believe It or Not

JOHN T. CAIN
Food and Drug Officer, Food and Drug Administration
Department of Health, Education, and Welfare
Washington, D. C.

Among the more unusual cases involving therapeutic devices investigated by the Food and Drug Administration is that of the fantastic orgone energy accumulator, formerly peddled by Dr. Wilhelm Reich of Rangeley, Maine. A resourceful and methodical man, Dr. Reich received his medical degree many years ago in Austria at the University of Vienna where he was prominently associated with Dr. Sigmund Freud of psychoanalytic fame. Always an individualist, Reich eventually surpassed Dr. Freud in imaginative qualities, and, during 1939 while still in Europe, he announced the discovery of a hitherto unknown and amazing energy that he chose to call "orgone."

After coming to the United States, Reich promptly invented a device for accumulating this all-powerful energy and for transmitting it to humans. This device was little shorter than a telephone booth and crudely constructed of alternate layers of wood or composition board, glass, and steel wool, with a metal lining. Reich proclaimed it a marvel of the ages and called it an orgone energy accumulator. His closest associate, also a physician, modestly described the device as "The most important single discovery in the history of medicine, bar none."

Reich rapidly produced other types of accumulators all constructed on the same principle and known as the "shooter box," "orgone energy blanket," and "orgone energy funnel." He attributed to them all the profound function of accumulating "orgone energy" from the atmosphere and transferring it to whatever sick patient might come under their exposure. The mysterious orgone energy, blue in color, visible in the sky, and present in every living organism, was trumpeted by Reich and his followers as having vast curative effect in disease conditions such as cancer, rheumatism, arthritis, high blood pressure, low blood pressure, anemia, and other afflictions both mental and physical.

Indeed, an entirely new glossary of medical terminology stemming from the word "orgone" was devised by Reich and his group colorfully to describe the use and results of treatment in the orgone energy accumulator. An extensive literature employing the new terminology was produced over the years, and Reich has seen to it that much of the literature was placed in prominent libraries throughout the country. Interwoven among the many orgone energy accumulator claims made in that literature is a certain mysticism amidst psychosomatic jargon and outright disease claims.

Throughout the Reichian literature on accumulators and orgone energy, the validity of the time-honored laws of thermodynamics and electricity is denied, yet Reich is quick to use these selfsame laws in his basic definitions and explanations of orgone energy. The user of an accumulator is warned by its inventor that water takes away all effects of orgone energy, and from this one could logically conclude that a bath or shower would certainly be followed by illness.

The Food and Drug Administration made an extensive investigation of all models of the orgone energy accumulator. In addition to tests in its own laboratories, outstanding physicists from outside the Government were engaged to determine whether any energy such as "orgone" is accumulated by these devices. Thorough tests were made by the best medical clinicians available to determine whether the devices exerted any beneficial effect in disease conditions. The results of all the clinical and physical tests conclusively established that orgone energy accumulators are worthless in the treatment of diseases and that no energy such as that described by Dr. Reich is detectable by any scientific method. The conclusion was inescapable that the devices were illegal under those provisions of the Federal Food, Drug, and Cosmetic Act that ban therapeutic devices from interstate commerce if their labeling is false or misleading in any particular.

A complaint for injunction was filed by the United States Attorney at Portland, Maine, and Dr. Reich and the other defendants were given every opportunity to make an appearance and defend their claims. Despite this, they elected to make no appearance in court, although they retained counsel and were fully advised. Their pretext was, in effect, that Reich and his asserted research with orgone energy accumulators are beyond the comprehension of the Food and Drug Administration and the Federal Court and not subject to their jurisdiction.

After consideration of all the facts, Federal Judge Clifford issued an injunction March 19, 1954, at Portland, against Dr. Reich, his wife, Ilse Ollendorff, and the Wilhelm Reich Foundation prohibiting further shipment of the accumulators in interstate commerce and requiring destruction of all promotional material containing instructions for the assembly and use of the enjoined devices. The bulk of Reich's writings were also required by the injunction to be withheld from distribution as labeling unless the violative references to orgone energy and other misbrandings were deleted. All accumulators rented out or otherwise under the control of the defendants were also required by the decree to be returned to Rangeley, Maine, and destroyed or salvaged under supervision of the Food and Drug Administration.

Investigation showed that Dr. Reich refused to comply with the orders of the Court, and the Government filed contempt proceedings against him and a New York doctor by the name of Michael Silvert. When arraigned July 26, 1955, in Federal Court at Portland, on a criminal contempt of court charge alleging failure to obey the injunction, Dr. Reich appeared with an entourage of his supporters, one of whom surrendered a loaded .38 caliber revolver to an officer outside of the courtroom. Upon his own request, Reich made an animated speech at the hearing complaining that the injunction was fabricated to kill him and his discoveries and to put him down in history as a scoundrel. He also took the Government counsel seriously to task and shouted that someone was trying to get at his laboratory and get his equations. Dr. Reich did not say whether these equations were the same ones referred to on page 76 of his book, *Ether, God and Devil*, where he wrote that he formulated a whole group of equations while half asleep.

Belatedly, Dr. Reich writes that he derived no benefits but only slander from orgone energy accumulators and indicates that he is trying to disassociate himself from those devices. Latest reports are that he has passed on to greener fields, using altered orgone energy accumulators, renamed "cloud busters," in the art of rainmaking. We have his word that he can create or destroy clouds, cause or stop rain, dispel fog, and otherwise profoundly affect meteorologic conditions by using the "cloud buster." He cautions operators of this device to withdraw to a safe distance if they feel dizzy or if their faces become blue or purple but avers that western deserts are again becoming moist and green under exposure to it.

As a fitting climax to a stormy career, Dr. Reich is now actively investigating the mysteries of interplanetary space and concerning himself with spaceships that he has heard but not seen. His substantial booklet, *Core*, volume VI, numbers 1 to 4, published recently, pictures frequent invasions of the earth by these machines from outer space, piloted by "Core Men" who are living people from outer space and powered by orgone energy.

A Representative of American Labor Looks at the Food and Drug Administration

LEE W. MINTON
*International President, Glass Bottle Blowers' Association
of the United States and Canada
Philadelphia, Pa.*

While Congress drags its feet, we are getting horse-and-buggy protection for our health and pocketbooks. What is needed is more "muscle" for the FDA!

The health of the people depends upon at least the full implementation of all existing health programs, each of which is an integral part of the whole problem. As trade unionists, we are not only concerned with in-plant health but with community health as well, i.e., the health of the worker's family and those around him in his community. Moreover, we are not only interested in adequate medical facilities and an adequate national health program for clinical treatment of disease and illness, but with an adequate program for preventing and control of disease and illness.

Like the spokes of a wheel, each program must be a strong and functional part if the whole program is to run smoothly and effectively. Unfortunately, one of the few spokes of the nation's wheel of health is badly in need of repair. I speak of the Food and Drug Administration.

Fifty years ago, Congress recognized that the American public was experiencing tragic consequences from being exposed to disease and insanitary foods; addiction or toxication from harmful drugs; fraud from mislabeled or adulterated foods, drugs, and cosmetics. To safeguard the American consumer from these effects, the Food and Drugs Act of 1906 was passed and the Food and Drug Administration (FDA) was created to establish standards and regulation of these industries.

Fifty years ago the situation was serious and was recognized as such. Today it is even more serious, but reactionary and selfish motivations of a few are hoodwinking Congress into virtually repealing its original legislative intent by inadequate appropriations to enforce the law.

Every home in this nation uses foods, drugs, and cosmetics over which FDA has jurisdiction. The value of products sold and distributed subject to FDA regulation is estimated at more than 60 billion annually with more than 100,000 establishments involved in manufacturing, processing, or distribution that are subject to inspection. Despite a population increase of more than 85,000,000 persons since 1906; despite a tenfold or more increase in the number of manufacturers, processors, shippers, and retailers; despite an almost fantastic change in the quality, quantity, and types of foods, drugs, and cosmetics through research and development, Congress, year in and year out, appropriates funds to an extent that would not even be sufficient to administer the Act adequately in the horse-and-buggy days of 1906.

The Federal Food, Drug, and Cosmetic Act of 1938 requires foods to be pure, wholesome, and free of any filth or decomposition to which disease can be traced. It requires drugs to be safe yet fully potent and properly labeled to direct proper use. It requires that cosmetics be safe for human use. It requires that all three of these meet established standards of quality and quantity when they are sold to the public.

Without even thinking of expanding over-all areas of responsibility and programs, an action that in itself is much needed and justified, FDA cannot even keep up with its previously established projects. Regular and periodic inspections by field personnel for enforcement purposes are ridiculously inadequate owing to lack of appropriations to hire necessary field personnel. Approximately 200 field inspectors are trying to cover 100,000 establishments, which has resulted in only 10 per cent of inspection coverage. At this rate, each establishment covered by the Act can expect an inspector once every 10 years. Of course, FDA has tried with its limited personnel to schedule inspections based upon relative urgency and need. Accordingly, some areas of coverage receive more inspections than others, but the fact remains that the law calls for full enforcement and hence full and complete inspections of all covered establishments. Of approximately 17,000 grain and flour establishments subject to inspection, the average yearly number inspected has been approximately 500. This in face of known and constantly recurring instances of sale and processing of diseased grain. As another illustration, the Amalgamated Meat Cutters and Butcher Workmen of North America-AFL have for years complained to government and industry that sick and diseased poultry is being processed and sold to the American housewife.

It is now common knowledge, except to the public in general, that filth and disease exists in certain parts of the poultry industry. Most shocking of all revelations is the high rate of diseased poultry that certain segments of this industry place on the dinner tables of American homes. All this is taking place despite the fact that science has proved that there is direct similarity of disease between poultry and man, and that man is more susceptible to contacting disease from poultry than from any other food source.

When a poultry operator is caught preying upon the public and jeopardizing the nation's health by selling diseased poultry, he quickly pleads guilty, or nolo-contendere (a legal defense of accepting criminal conviction), and pays a nominal statutory fine. He then hurries back to his filthy and insanitary plant to spread more disease knowing that an FDA inspector will not reach him again, on his long list of establishments to inspect, for months to come, if ever.

These are but two examples of how thousands of food processors are deliberately jeopardizing the health of this nation. Similar situations exist in the drug and cosmetic industry. Traffic in adulterated drugs, even more lethal in their effect upon human lives, is becoming more widespread due to consumer ignorance of labels or preparations. The same holds true for cosmetics. Naturally, reputable food, drug, and cosmetic concerns are not involved. They never think of illegal marketing nor have any reason to subordinate public interest to their own profit status.

Rather it is the "fly-by-night" manufacturer or processor who, in cahoots with the disreputable butcher or pharmacist, prey on the public. There are so many of these little and scattered operators that the job of proper investigation becomes more difficult and requires more manpower to cover such a vastly scattered area than ordinarily realized.

Apart from the very important health aspects of this over-all problem of inadequate FDA inspections, there are also economic aspects involved. As trade unionists representing the largest individual group of consumers, we must insist that the Act be fully implemented to prevent fraud upon the consuming public. Not only have the health responsibilities of FDA lagged far behind but the "economic responsibilities" have of necessity only received passing attention. By "economic responsibilities" the law was intended to protect the consuming public from being swindled by disreputable food, drug, and cosmetic manufacturers or processors who fail to maintain minimum quality and quantity standards. It is impossible to determine accurately the hundreds of millions of dollars lost each year by the consumer as a result of deliberate cheating in the quality and quantity of foods, drugs, and cosmetics. In adulterated drugs alone, the estimate runs from $50,000,000 to $120,000,000 in yearly traffic.

Also in the area of economic responsibility a serious problem is recurring that results indirectly from that of inadequate FDA investigation activities and that relates to the working conditions under which insanitary foods and adulterated drugs are manufactured or processed. Although FDA does not have jurisdiction over working conditions in these industries, it does attempt to establish programs for plant cleanliness as such would relate to purity of foods, drugs, and cosmetics. Working among filth and disease is no less damaging to the healthfulness of human beings than it is to the healthfulness of foods. The same selfish profit motivations that go so far in jeopardizing the health of this nation are also undermining the health of employees working in these "fly-by-night" installations. Proof of this relationship is evidenced by a recent case of a diseased food product found to be manufactured in a "home industry." "Home industries" date to the sweatshop era when workers were forced to toil in cellars and lofts for long hours under horrible conditions. Since not all of these leeches are able to operate openly and in flagrant violation of the law, many locate themselves in cellars, lofts, and garages and operate not only in violation of the Federal Food, Drug and Cosmetic Act but in violation of other federal, state, and municipal health and safety laws.

Fortunately, to correct the problem, no lengthy and time consuming task of enacting legislation is involved. The necessary legislation and enabling authority exist. All that is required is for Congress to appropriate sufficient funds for inspection purposes, so that the Food and Drug Administration can properly discharge its responsibilities in protecting the public, its health as well as its pocketbook.

Public Health Activities of the
Food and Drug Administration

IRVIN KERLAN

Division of Medicine, Food and Drug Administration
Department of Health, Education, and Welfare
Washington, D. C.

The Food and Drug Administration, during the past 50 years, has provided protection of the public health and welfare as its fundamental responsibility and function through control of foods and drugs in interstate commerce. With the passage of the Federal Food, Drug, and Cosmetic Act of 1938, protection was extended to control new drugs, dangerous drugs, devices, and injurious cosmetics, and protection improved with respect to foods and drugs. With these additional safeguards, the physician is aided in his efforts to prevent and treat disease. The provisions of this law dealing with the disclosure of active ingredients of drugs, adequate directions for use, and warnings against misuse contribute to the intelligent purchase and use of drugs.

Safeguards against variations in the strength, quality, and purity of drugs are of fundamental importance. Similarly, the requirement that the labels of foods offered for special dietary use bear adequate information to inform the purchaser, enables the physician and consumer to evaluate the indications for use of such foods.

A major area of health service to the public is the processing of new-drug applications setting forth evidence of the safety of the drug as submitted by manufacturers. The gravity of appropriate handling of these applications before releasing the drugs for use is complicated by the statutory requirement that the review be completed within a limited, fixed time. With the increasing numbers of highly potent and effective drugs being submitted currently for consideration, public health is paramount in the decision to allow such drugs to be marketed.

An invaluable service to the public is the pretesting for purity and potency before distribution of six of the most important antibiotics and insulin, as well as certifying the safety of coal-tar dyes for use in foods, drugs, or cosmetics. Regulation of the retail sale of dangerous prescription drugs is another important health protection service furnished by the Food and Drug Administration.

During the past 20 years, chemotherapeutic agents have been introduced that have changed the methods of prevention and treatment of many diseases. The availability of the sulfonamides and antibiotics under the new-drug provisions and certification sections of the Act has markedly influenced the treatment of such serious infectious diseases as streptococcal infections, syphilis, gonorrhea, and tuberculosis, with a rewarding reduction of mortality from these causes.

Despite all of the precautions taken, serious illnesses and injuries resulting from unsuspected defects in commercial products have been encountered. None of the products involved was suspected of causing harm until an appreciable number of persons had become ill. The frequency and seriousness of these occurrences have become a matter of concern to those in the Public Health Service and the Food and Drug Administration who have responsibility for protecting the public from injurious substances in foods, drugs, and cosmetics and for controlling diseases or injuries arising from ingestion of harmful foods, drugs, and other hazardous articles. A recent incident that was encountered and controlled was the appearance of *Salmonella* infections in infants, traced in 16 states to the feeding of dried egg yolk. The product was voluntarily recalled from the market by the manufacturer when it became apparent that the food was associated with the illness.

Another major nationwide incident was the investigation by the Food and Drug Administration of the association of blood dyscrasias with chloramphenicol, which resulted in modified labeling of this drug in the interest of the physician and his patient.

A third major event was the appearance of convulsions in infants maintained on a liquid infant food. This involvement was corrected by a change in manufacture of the product. In this instance, with reports of illness from the Arkansas State Board of Health, the Food and Drug Administration undertook an investigation that resulted in the recall from the market of all material bearing the codes associated with this type of illness.

These cases are not the first of their kind, but they typify the examples that point up the need for prompt reporting of any unusual occurrences of diseases or injury to responsible health officials in order to safeguard others and to bring about an early correction of the health problem.

The general use of the many potent and effective therapeutic agents now available emphasizes the need to learn promptly of any serious untoward effects associated with their use. Should adverse effects be encountered with a product and revealed to the Food and Drug Administration, necessary safeguards to protect the patient, the physician, the hospital, the drug manufacturer, and the distributor would be effectively carried out. This has led, in the past few months, to the Pilot Study on Reporting Adverse Reactions to Drugs sponsored by the Food and Drug Administration and American Association of Medical Record Librarians in cooperation with the American Medical Association and the American Society of Hospital Pharmacists. Through this study, methodology can be developed for continued general submission of reports as well as their evaluation, dissemination, and program development. This cooperative undertaking may serve as the basis for a wide extension of this activity at a later date.

With the decline of infectious diseases through immunization procedures and improved sanitation measures, poisoning from household chemicals, including drugs, has come into focus more prominently as a health problem. The Food and Drug Administration has been engaged in this area since the passage of the Federal Caustic Poison Act in 1927. With the active participation of the American Academy of Pediatrics, the American Medical Association, the American Public Health Association, health departments, hospitals, pharmacists, the pharmaceutical and chemical industries, and governmental and voluntary health agencies, measurable inroads are being made. Additional recognized needs, however, should be implemented to provide optimal protection.

With the continued cooperation and advice of public health officers, physicians, and other professional experts, the public can be assured of safe and nutritious foods and safe and effective drugs and devices.

The Food and Drug Administration—Cheap Insurance

WILLIAM R. JESTER
Department of Health, Education, and Welfare
Food and Drug Administration
Division of Antibiotics
Washington, D. C.

It has been just a few years since the average American family grew and processed its own food, mixed most of its drugs (except those prescribed by the physician and compounded by him or by the local apothecary), and made most of its simple cosmetics from the berries and plants that grew on the farm. Not so today! The average family has moved from the vegetable garden, the smokehouse, the barn, the granary, and the kitchen to the rumpus room. Hundreds of ready-to-eat foods and literally thousands of external and internal nostrums are readily available. There are myriads of cosmetic mixtures that are intended for men, women, and children.

The physician is offered drugs of all descriptions—gases, capsules, powders, tablets, granules, solutions, suspensions, suppositories, pills, and ointments packaged in bombs, jets, bullets, cartridges, insufflators, tubes, cans, foil, glass, and plastic. The old time apothecary is almost extinct. Today, in most cases he can fill his prescriptions by removing the manufacturers' labels and replacing them with his prescription labels or by transferring pills from the market containers to his own pillboxes.

With the transfer to mass production, the consumer lost control over the wholesomeness, soundness, purity, and safety of most of his food products and over the purity, safety, and effectiveness of his drugs. In fact, before Congress passed our first Federal food and drug laws in 1906, poisonous substances were used extensively in food and drug products, and many people suffered serious and sometimes fatal consequences because of misrepresentations made in the labeling of widely advertised drugs.

The great majority of the manufacturers and distributors who are subject to regulations by the Food and Drug Administration are competent and honest. However, there is a small element, as in most occupations, who will cheat for personal gain, and others who are indifferent to insanitary conditions. Included in this group are the ignorant, the negligent, and the willfully criminal who have no regard for the welfare of the consumer. A few examples that we encounter are those who use polluted water for washing food products and those who process, pack, or store foods and drugs under loathsome and indescribably filthy conditions. Some have sold mercury-treated grain as food. Others have added poisons to food in an attempt to check spoilage that could have been avoided by sanitary practices. It is common to find water or cheap fillers added to expensive foods. Substances are sometimes found in cosmetics that have not been adequately tested for safety. Worthless drug concoctions, nails, and pieces of colored glass and photographic projectors have been represented as cures for tuberculosis, epilepsy, diabetes, and cancer. Cheats of this sort result in irreparable harm or even death. Ascorbic acid has been sold as cortisone, lactose as streptomycin, and aspirin as penicillin, thus depriving patients of medications prescribed for serious conditions. A few renegade pharmacists take seriously their nickname of "Doc" and dispense dangerous and habit-forming drugs without physicians' prescriptions.

These are the kind of people that the Food and Drug Administration tries to apprehend—or "educate"—before they can foist their spurious and dangerous wares or their "services" on the American public. It is a gigantic task, especially when we consider that there are now in this country—not counting those who operate completely underground—almost 100,000 known establishments (and new ones spring up daily) that manufacture, process, pack, or store foods, drugs, therapeutic devices, or cosmetics having a sales value estimated at 60 billion dollars annually. This amount is approximately one fourth of all average American families' income. In addition to these, thousands of foreign manufacturers send their products to us from the four corners of the earth, all of which are subject to examination by the Food and Drug Administration before being permitted to enter the country.

Few people realize the role played by the Food and Drug Administration in their daily lives. In fact, it is likely that not more than one in each hundred people in the average American town has ever heard of the work of the Administration. Yet, no service rendered by the Federal Government has a more profound effect on the health and welfare of the American people, because each of us daily uses products that are regulated by the Administration. That the average consumer does not know of the operations of the Food and Drug Administration may be due in part to the fact that its protection currently costs him only about three pennies per year. Because the annual budget (currently $5,484,000) is so small when compared to most government agencies, the average taxpayer has not taken the time to acquaint himself with its operations. It is less, in fact, than the amount each of a great many companies regulated by FDA spends annually for advertising or for research.

Recognizing the need, a large number of the regulated industries, local and national civic groups, and just plain consumers have recommended that the Congressional appropriations for the Food and Drug Administration be increased substantially—up to four times—to safeguard the public more effectively against misbranded or adulterated foods, drugs, therapeutic devices, and cosmetics. If its annual cost per person were increased from 3 to 12 cents, or more, it would still be cheap health, accident, and life insurance.

Preparation for Disaster

F. LESLIE HART

Chief, Food and Drug Administration
Department of Health, Education, and Welfare
Boston District, Boston, Mass.

Disasters alter routine activities. Almost every field district of the Food and Drug Administration has, at one time or another, been forced to lay aside all other activities to cope with a major flood, fire, or hurricane. When such disasters occur, the normal forces of State and local health agencies are overtaxed, and there is a pressing need for experienced personnel to aid these agencies. The Food and Drug Administration has always integrated its men with the State and local units and functioned under a single direction with these units.

In 1936, and again in 1937, heavy floods occurred in various parts of the country. In 1938, hurricane-induced floods ravaged wide areas in New England. The Kansas river system inundated metropolitan Kansas City in 1951. Hurricanes Carol and Edna, which sent floodwaters raging through Providence, Rhode Island, in 1954, and Diane, which flooded large areas of New England and Pennsylvania in 1955, are still fresh in our memory today.

The 1937 Ohio River floods required the services of 44 Food and Drug inspectors and chemists to serve with and assist local officials. The 1938 hurricane drained all the inspectional staff of the Food and Drug Administration's Boston District and a considerable number of men from the New York and Philadelphia Districts. The 18 inspectors and chemists comprising the Food and Drug Administration's Kansas City District, along with 20 more from other Food and Drug Administration District offices formed a trained Federal unit that cooperated with local staffs who were policing the disposition of foods and drugs damaged in the Kansas City flood. Hurricane Carol in 1954, and Diane in 1955, again required the services of the entire professional staff of the Boston District in the flooded areas. In fact, Diane's scope was so wide that the New York and Buffalo Districts and the Food and Drug Administration's Central Offices, located in Washington, all provided men.

The first duty of health officers and regulatory officials in the public health field, following immediate rescue and relief activities, is to ascertain the fate of stocks of foods and drugs exposed to these catastrophes and to prevent the sale or distribution of polluted or deteriorated lots. This involves locating such lots, destroying those that are unfit, and supervising salvage operations.

Even while the flooded areas in Kansas City were still under water, experienced Federal, State, or city inspectors were out in rowboats making preliminary surveys. Railway lines and yards were located and inundated freight cars spotted. At preliminary conferences, plans were quickly formulated that welded the resources of all regulatory agencies into one coordinated inspection force using the District office of the Food and Drug Administration as a coordination center. The Food and Drug Administration force acted under the authority of two State and two or more city laws. The embargo powers and the emergency police authority of State and local agencies were used to halt traffic in foods and drugs affected until they could be inspected and their salvage supervised. Food and Drug Administration men quickly trained those State and city sanitarians and health officers who had no experience with food and drug inspection. State, city, and Federal men were used interchangeably, with over-all operations under State control, except metropolitan Kansas City, which was under the supervision of the Health Departments of the two sister cities.

In addition to stocks of foods and drugs in wholesale and retail establishments, Kansas City had thousands of railroad cars caught in yards or in transit that were immersed wholly or partly in filthy flood waters. These cars had to be moved quickly to facilitate track repairs. Food and Drug Administration inspectors were assigned to each of the railroads concerned to examine the contents of each freight car as rapidly as railroad crews could locate them. Industries whose stocks were involved cooperated wholeheartedly in the task of preventing unfit foods and drugs getting back into commercial channels.

The coordinated work brought results no one group could have achieved alone. The disposal of the vast stock of foods and drugs, estimated at some $150 million and including the destruction, denaturing, or salvaging of the equivalent of about 3400 carloads of food, had been effected without a single authenticated case of disease or illness traceable to flood-damaged or spoiled goods.

The 1954 hurricane in Providence offered different problems. Except for minor damage in Massachusetts and Connecticut, the damage was confined to metropolitan Providence. Hurricane Carol struck at high tide, forcing ocean waters up the Providence River. This formed a water dam that caused the sewage-laden river and its tributaries to inundate all of downtown Providence to the second story level. The city was without telephone, light, or power service. Aid was at once offered to the Rhode Island and Providence Health Departments by the Boston District. This was accepted, and a coordinated work plan was set up.

The work plan assigned coverage of wholesale grocers, food warehouses, cold storage plants, and wholesale and retail drug establishments to Food and Drug Administration inspectors; wholesale meat houses to State health inspectors; and retail groceries, meat shops, bars, and restaurants to the City Health Department. Work occurring outside of Providence would be assigned either to State men or to Federal men.

One immediate problem was the disposal of the large amounts of damaged provisions and drugs that were being shoveled out of stores and dumped in the street. The city located a suitable area; the Food and Drug Administration, through its liaison with the Army, obtained trucks, bulldozers, and other equipment together with operating manpower; and the city, with the technical assistance of the Public Health Service, established a sanitary landfill dump, properly policed to prevent pilferage. A relatively small amount of the damaged merchandise, mainly canned foods, was salvageable. A private salvage operator set up a sanitizing plant outside of Providence, and all salvageable goods went through this plant, under the supervision of a Food and Drug Administration inspector.

Hurricane Edna struck on September 11. Little damage was done by Edna, the principal effect being to delay salvage operations. Total loss of foods, drugs, and cosmetics as a consequence of the two hurricanes was estimated to amount to 10 million dollars.

As in Kansas City, not a single authenticated case of disease attributable to flood-contaminated food was reported in Providence. This is a remarkable achievement, considering that the floodwaters were heavily contaminated with raw sewage. The State and local authorities, perplexed by their own problems, gladly assigned the direction of over-all activities of all units to the experienced Food and Drug Administration representative. Here flood damage was concentrated in a relatively small area, the State capitol, and both State and local Government offices were in the same city, greatly facilitating coordination activities.

The 1955 floods were different. Torrential rains that were triggered by hurricane Diane overflowed rivers in six States of the New England and of the Middle Atlantic area.

Federal Food and Drug inspectors near river cities were ordered to change their itineraries and prepare to move in if there was a flood. Food and Drug Administration Districts immediately established close contact with the United States Army Engineers Flood Control offices, State and city police headquarters, State and city Health Departments, and State and Federal Civil Defense Administration to keep abreast of the situation. Coordinated operating bases were established in many disaster areas. United States Food and Drug inspectors became members of teams whose job it was to safeguard food and drug supplies.

In all areas, the Federal inspectors were deputized under State or local law, exercising embargo powers under the State Food and Drug law. Police and military personnel were assigned the job of guarding unprotected establishments and dumps. Governors, Mayors, and State Civil Defense Administrators provided trucks and other equipment; the local Health Officers furnished advice on sanitation or methods for destroying unfit merchandise.

The 1955 floods were unique in that very little attempt was made at salvage. The flood deposited enormous quantities of silt and debris, making salvage almost impossible. Waters rose fairly slowly, allowing railroads time to move freight cars. Some States prohibited the movement of flood-contaminated foods and drugs unless they were first sanitized. This was impossible in most instances because of the low water supply. The total loss in foods, drugs, and cosmetics probably reached $30 million.

It may be well to have a plan of operation prepared to cope with these natural disasters. This can well be made a part of prior planning for civil defense. It is essential in such a plan to recognize promptly the need for trained assistance and to call upon all organizations to supplement existing forces. Normal local facilities for refuse disposal are inadequate; prompt disposal of contaminated or spoiled food or damaged drugs is essential to protect public health; and medical, police, and labor forces must augment the facilities that are in existence when any disaster strikes.

126

The Food and Drug Administration
Inspector and Chemist

FRANKLIN D. CLARK

Chief Inspector, Division of Field Operations
Food and Drug Administration
Department of Health, Education, and Welfare
Washington, D. C.

Nowhere in the world are the food, drug, and cosmetic supplies available to the consumer as well protected as they are in the United States. This is in no small measure due to the dedication of the food and drug inspectors and chemists who daily carry out their various duties in the laboratories and on field assignments. These men and women are public servants of the highest order. Without their unflagging interest, ingenuity, and accuracy, the American consumer would soon become the victim of *caveat emptor*.

The Food and Drug inspector is the eyes and ears of the Food and Drug Administration and is the "front line" in maintaining the integrity of foods, drugs, and cosmetics. He inspects production and distribution establishments; investigates injury complaints and outbreaks of poisoning; and reports evidence of violation of the Food, Drug, and Cosmetic Act, the Filled Milk Act, the Caustic Poison Act, and the Tea Act. He examines the sanitary conditions in manufacturing establishments and the techniques and controls employed in the processing, labeling, and packaging of foods, drugs, and cosmetics. His contacts with the public include interviews with consumers, industry executives, production and research chemists, and other persons connected with the manufacturing, transportation, warehousing, and retailing branches of these important commodities. These duties furnish him with a fascinating insight into the history of these commodities from the raw materials to the market basket of the American housewife.

The Food and Drug chemist stands as an equally important protector against impure foods and impotent drugs. He confirms and supplements the inspector's observations by analysis of samples of the foods, drugs, or cosmetics for composition, for small quantities of extraneous material, for dangerous chemicals, or new and novel ingredients. He is an expert in specialized fields of food technology and food and drug chemistry, where he must exercise ingenuity and resourcefulness when confronted with the many problems peculiar to these fields. As he becomes experienced, he enjoys the opportunity to devise new and original methods of analysis or to improve old methods. He engages in research in such interesting fields as new drugs and chemical additives to foods, utilizing spectrophotometric, chromatographic, and microanalytic techniques.

The food and drug inspectors and chemists have, of necessity, had to "grow" with the recent swift technologic advances in the food, drug, and cosmetic industries. Industrial research, modernized plant facilities, and expanded control procedures, as well as the competitive conditions of an expanding economy have resulted in the swift development of new and potent drugs and of significant changes in food and drug processing. This challenge has been met through research, study, and resourcefulness. New inspectional techniques have been devised to keep pace with these changes and to uncover the skillfully concealed violations of the "fringe" operators. New laboratory procedures have been devised to demonstrate scientifically the composition of foods, drugs, and cosmetics where new ingredients, processes, or composition have rendered recognized methods obsolete. The inspectors and chemists, with their co-workers in pharmacology, bacteriology, microbiology, medicine, and related fields, are establishing landmarks in the advance of our food, drug, and cosmetic supplies.

These public servants are fully aware of their tremendous responsibility. Their pride and satisfaction in the essential job they are doing together is great. The security of the contents of our medicine chests, our refrigerators, and our pantries is in good hands.

Household Poisoning

BERNARD DAVIDOW
Chief, Acute Toxicity Branch
Division of Pharmacology, Food and Drug Administration
Department of Health, Education, and Welfare
Washington, D. C.

The Food and Drug Administration, through its responsibilities under the Federal Food, Drug, and Cosmetic Act and the Caustic Poison Act, is concerned with the high incidence of poisoning that occurs in the home. Many home products involved contain agents that are recognized in industry as being hazardous, but when sold in retail trade are purchased by persons unaware of their potential harmfulness. Even the family doctor finds it difficult to keep abreast of the many new toxic substances, their trade names, and the formulations in which they occur as household chemicals. To correct this unfortunate situation, the Food and Drug Administration is developing a more forceful program based on legal and educational measures. Part of the program consists of working with other groups interested in reducing the risks of accidental poisoning. The development of poison control centers and the reporting to the Administration of untoward drug reactions are examples of cooperation between government and nongovernment institutions. The data collected through such activities may provide the basis for changes in Administration policy or interpretation regarding labeling of products frequently incriminated in accidental poisonings. An unusually high incidence of accidents with a particular product seems to imply inadequate labeling in that the label is not clear or conspicuous, does not contain a statement of active ingredients, does not provide adequate directions for use, or does not contain adequate warning or cautions regarding misuse or storage of the product.

An educational program is also being directed to reach the individual in the home. A leaflet, *Protect Your Family Against Poisoning*, has been distributed to individuals and interested groups. Such literature is designed to make the individual aware of the harmful potentialities of drugs and household chemical products and to encourage protective measures, which include reading labels carefully, following directions, discarding old prescriptions, and keeping toxic materials out of the reach of children.

As a further service to the medical profession, Food and Drug medical officers and pharmacologists have always been available for consultation regarding problems of toxicology. Many phone calls have been received from anxious physicians regarding emergency poisoning cases. Frequently the physician inquires as to the active ingredient in a particular product, the toxic dose, and the recommended treatment. Too frequently, he fails to recognize that constituents other than the active ingredients must be considered in appraising the toxicity of a particular product. The fact that so-called inert solvents frequently comprise 95 per cent of a formulation makes them at times a more serious problem than the active component.

In most instances, our pharmacologists are acquainted with the general composition of products, such as polishes, pesticides, cleansers, and proprietary medicines, and they can offer an opinion as to the probable composition of the article in question, the likelihood of this material to cause harm, and the indicated emergency treatment.

Although we do not wish to minimize the hazards of household poisons, we would like to call attention to the fact that the mortality in comparison to the incidence of poisoning is fortunately low. There is at the present time about 1 fatality to every 100 cases.

Because there are no specific antidotes for the vast majority of poisons, delaying absorption, gastric lavage, and the treatment of various symptoms as they arise are the usual recommendations. If specific antidotes are available, they are recommended as the need arises. In any case, the physician is cautioned against overzealous treatment that may do more harm than good to the patients who have been poisoned.

In this manner the Food and Drug Administration serves not only as a regulatory agency, but also as an organization dedicated to the encouragement, through education, of sound practices in the home, in industry, and in the medical profession.

VII. FOOD AND DRUG ADMINISTRATION AND AGRICULTURE

The Pharmacologic Problems of Crop-protecting Chemicals

O. GARTH FITZHUGH

Chief, Chronic Toxicity Branch
Division of Pharmacology, Food and Drug Administration
Department of Health, Education, and Welfare
Washington, D. C.

The introduction of pesticides to the agricultural market in ever increasing chemical complexity, quantity, and numbers has created a widespread interest in the possible dangers of consuming foods treated with these chemicals. By and large they are poisons, and injury can be expected when the dose ingested is excessive. Our major pharmacologic problem, however, is not the determination of the rather crude end point represented by death, but rather an evaluation of the continued use of the agricultural products treated with normal amounts of the pesticide. This hazard is dependent more specifically on the injury produced by ingestion of small amounts over long periods of time. We cannot compress into a few months an experiment dealing with a lifetime process. Our greatest problem therefore arises from the fact that evidences of safety must be obtained from the feeding of laboratory animals over their life span and then observing the effects produced by the chemical.

The allusion to fatal or nonfatal illnesses attributed to pesticides carries with it the implication of an acute exposure to pesticidal chemicals. This can occur in people who apply the pesticide. The hazards involved to these individuals are obvious and can be corrected. It is more difficult to evaluate the subtle effects of these chemicals, and the grounds for uneasiness in the past have rested upon the fear of the introduction of new insecticides into commercial practice without adequate testing. Public Law 518 is intended to prevent this possibility. However, when the chronic effects have been fairly well-established by a petitioner for a tolerance, the problem of more extensive use of a particular chemical, new uses, or its carry over into other products as an unintentional additive, may be cause for concern.

The type of toxicity that may be exhibited as the result of administering low dosages of a pesticide over prolonged periods cannot always be anticipated. However, our experience to date indicates that several significant trends have developed. These are valuable in arriving at a pharmacologic basis of the hazards of residues. In the first group are the pesticides that produce injury in some specific organ. The chief members of this group are the chlorinated hydrocarbons. Histopathologic changes may appear at very low levels of feeding. For instance, dichlorodiphenyltrichloroethane (DDT) at a dosage level of 5 parts per million in the diet of rats produces slight liver changes. Pesticides of this group are likely to leave significant quantities, either of the parent compound or of a toxic metabolite, stored in the tissues. Considerable speculation has arisen regarding the toxicologic implications of the accumulation of these pesticides in adipose tissue. It appears to be a reasonable assumption that adipose tissue, which has many important functions, can be influenced by the presence of cumulative poisons. At least from the experimental data, evidence to date indicates that there is a close parallelism between the storage propensity of a pesticide and its ability to injure. The amount of accumulation in the tissues and the rate of disappearance of a toxicant has another important bearing in terms of residue hazard, as illustrated by the indirect residues in meat, which assume the same importance as the direct residues on fruits and vegetables. Even more important is the excretion of the pesticide or its metabolite in milk.

In a second group are the pesticides that are capable of producing profound physiologic changes without causing visible histologic changes. The principal representatives of this group are the organic phosphates. So far as is known now, these chemicals have their major toxic effects as anticholinesterase agents and produce their abnormal physiologic influence through the enzyme system. As well as being potent, acute poisons, these pesticides exert cumulative effects and lead to a progressive decrease in the cholinesterase activity of the tissues. Some of these agents produce toxic effects in animals in quantities as low as 0.1 parts per million in the diet. Consequently, the responsibility of the Food and Drug Administration to set tolerances that will insure a safe food supply is not being taken lightly.

Still another pharmacologic aspect is the effect of two or more pesticides contaminating the same food. Several pesticides may be used at different steps in the production of the food crop, and all or part of each chemical may remain until the food is ready for consumption. It has been shown in the laboratories of the Food and Drug Administration that the effects of certain pesticides are additive, and therefore the sum total of all pesticides on a raw agricultural crop assumes importance.

The final step is the translation of animal studies to the probable effect on man. Since animals, for the most part, are more resistant to toxic chemicals than man, a margin of safety is necessary. In the consideration of such a margin of safety, the pharmacologist must take into account factors, such as strain and species susceptibility, sex differences, state of health, and all auxiliary factors that may lead to a misinterpretation of the true hazard to man. A conservative evaluation of the hazards involved does not lead to the necessity of restricting the use of pesticides below the limits where they would serve a useful purpose.

The Food and Drug Interpretation of the Miller Pesticide Residue Amendment to the Food, Drug, and Cosmetic Act

W. B. RANKIN
Assistant to the Commissioner
Food and Drug Administration
Department of Health, Education, and Welfare
Washington, D. C.

A Federal law enacted in 1954 provides a new method for determining how much poisonous agricultural spray or dust may remain safely on crops. It is the Pesticide Chemicals Amendment to the Federal Food, Drug, and Cosmetic Act. It also is known as the Miller Amendment in honor of Congressman A. L. Miller who sponsored it.

This legislation was needed because of great agricultural changes in the last decade. For more than a generation, we have recognized that poisonous chemicals are necessary to control disease, insects, and other pests of plants. At first only a few were used. Bordeaux mixture and Paris green were early standbys of the farmer. By 1940 several more were available, but most of the chemicals then available were well-known compounds.

World War II stimulated unprecedented research on insecticides. DDT was developed for use throughout the world in typhus control, and when released for civilian use it proved more effective against a host of insects than traditional poisons. Soon other organic chemicals very useful against pests were being synthesized and marketed in volume. Today more than a hundred basic poisons are used by growers; they are available in approximately 40,000 formulations; millions of pounds of pesticides are produced each year.

For decades public health authorities have tested crops to see that the pesticide residues left on them are safe. The quantity of each of the early poisons that could remain on a crop without hazard had been determined informally. Formal tolerances could be set after a public hearing, but the procedure was cumbersome. It did not keep pace with the rapid advances in agriculture. A convenient method of setting a safe tolerance for residues that could remain on crops was essential; the method had to be one that would result in public announcement of the tolerance so that everyone concerned would know it and could abide by it.

The Miller Pesticide Chemical Amendment was the answer. It amends the Federal Food, Drug, and Cosmetic Act, which requires food in interstate commerce to be wholesome and safe. The amendment gives a convenient procedure for deciding what pesticide residue may remain without harm to the wholesomeness and safety of a crop. It works this way: The person who wishes to promote a pesticide chemical secures evidence about its toxicity to animals. (Chronic toxicity data are especially important.) He secures evidence about the amount of chemical that remains on food after its use. He submits these facts, and others, to the U. S. Food and Drug Administration, which enforces the Food, Drug, and Cosmetic Act, and requests the Administration to set a formal tolerance for safe residues of the chemical.

Simultaneously the promoter asks the U. S. Department of Agriculture to certify that the chemical is useful.

When the Food and Drug Administration has the certificate of usefulness, it determines what amount of the chemical may be consumed daily for a lifetime without any harm. If this quantity of chemical is needed on crops, it is set as the tolerance level to be permitted. If crops can be protected without leaving this much chemical, a lower level that meets the needs of agriculture is set as the tolerance. If the chemical is too toxic to remain on food in any amount, the tolerance is set at zero. If the chemical is relatively innocuous so that any foreseeable use of it will not be a hazard to the public health, it is exempted from the requirement of a tolerance.

The Commissioner of Food and Drugs announces the tolerance or exemption formally by signing an Order and publishing it in the *Federal Register*.

When a tolerance is set for a pesticide chemical this means that: (1) Crops in interstate commerce should bear no more than the tolerance level of residue. Higher residues make the crops contraband. (2) Residues within the tolerance are safe. This is established by adequate chronic toxicity studies on test animals. (3) The chemical is useful. This is shown by the certificate of usefulness from the Department of Agriculture. (4) When used properly, the chemical will leave residues within the safe level. The Food and Drug Administration will not set a tolerance unless there is evidence that it can be met.

The Pesticide Chemicals Amendment was drafted with the assistance and support of farm groups, the agricultural chemical industry, and food law enforcement officials. Already it has proved its worth. Tolerances or exemptions are in effect for more than 70 of the pesticides in common use. Within the next few months most of the remaining chemicals now used will be cleared under the new procedure. As new pesticides are developed or new uses are proposed for old ones, they will be handled under it.

The Food and Drug Administration has examined agricultural commodities for many years to see that they are free from unsafe chemical residues. This kind of checking will continue. The new amendment does not change the basic legal requirement that food shall be pure.

An important benefit from the new law is that it should dispel fears that consumers are in danger from the chemicals used by farmers on their crops. The formal tolerances publicly announced and enforced as thoroughly as the old informal ones are an effective guarantee that the American people continue to have one of the safest food supplies in the world.

Control of Veterinary Drugs under the Federal Food, Drug, and Cosmetic Act

JOHN H. COLLINS
Veterinary Medical Director, Chief, Veterinary Medical Branch
Division of Medicine, Food and Drug Administration
Department of Health, Education, and Welfare
Washington, D. C.

Few persons are cognizant of the fact that the same drugs that have been found useful in preventing and alleviating the ills of man are also of value in the prophylaxis and therapy of similar illnesses that afflict our animals and poultry. This fact was recognized by the Congress of the United States when it included in the statutory definition of a drug the phrase, "for man or other animals." Furthermore, the standards and specifications for identity, purity, sterility, and potency of drugs prescribed in the *Pharmacopoeia of the United States* and the *National Formulary* are fully as applicable to drugs for animals as to the same drugs for man.

The value of the combined livestock and poultry industries in the United States has been estimated at more than 15 billion dollars. This industry suffers an annual loss of approximately 3 billion dollars from disease and parasitism. Calculations based on published data indicate a sales value in drugs for animal use of more than 160 million dollars yearly, an increase of 50 million dollars in seven years.

The foregoing facts and figures when taken into consideration with the knowledge that there is a daily increase of 85,000 human mouths in the world in need of animal protein* points up the importance of our animal population in relation to the human population.

New drugs for animals, like those for man, must be shown to be safe when used as directed before they can legally be marketed in interstate commerce. This

---

* WHO (World Health Organization) Newsletter, *8*:11–12, November-December, 1955.

requires a new drug application as provided for in the Federal Food, Drug, and Cosmetic Act. In addition, however, there is one further requirement. If the drug, when used in food-producing animals, is capable of producing residues in edible tissues, the applicant (manufacturer) must prove that those residues are within safe limits for human consumers. If the drug is to affect a physiologic function, such as increased growth or weight gains, feed consumption or utilization, milk production or egg production, i.e., not actually required in the production of food (from animal origin), the applicant must show that the edible portions are entirely free of any added drug residue or drug effect at the time of slaughtering the animals.

There seems to be an ever-increasing number of drugs that are used for such purposes. The effect of such practices on our food supply is a matter of concern, not only to the public generally, but also to regulatory officials, public health officials, animal husbandmen, and scientists generally, both in and out of the Government. While the economic advantage and importance of these developments to the producer of livestock, poultry, milk, eggs, and wool cannot be overlooked, they must, in our opinion, take a secondary position to the legal requirement that our food supply must be free from unnecessary poisonous or deleterious substances.

The drugs that are used or proposed for use in animal and poultry feeding for their physiologic effect are, for the most part, highly potent compounds, capable, in very small amounts, of causing profound changes in the body structures or functions of the animals to which they are fed. The possibility that residual amounts of such compounds in human food may produce adverse effects upon consumers makes necessary a thorough investigation of any chemical or drug proposed for use in animal feeding.

The question has been asked, "What types of data are regarded as adequate to establish the safety of a proposed practice in this field?" A categorical answer cannot be given. The data, of course, must be characterized by scientific accuracy, comprehensibility, reproducibility, and those other factors that are inherent in a well-planned, scientifically controlled study. They should be such as to remove any reasonable doubt in the minds of scientifically trained experts that the foods produced from animals on the feeding program are free of added poisonous or deleterious substances resulting from the practice. In general, except for "prescription-only labels" and "habit-forming warnings," the Act contains the same provisions for control of veterinary drugs as it does for human drugs. They must be properly labeled with all mandatory information and be free of false or misleading claims.

Nerve Poisons

JOHN P. FRAWLEY
Assistant Chief, Chronic Toxicity Branch
Division of Pharmacology, Food and Drug Administration
Department of Health, Education, and Welfare
Washington, D. C.

A few years ago the mention of the term "nerve poison" was enough to raise the eyebrow of even the most conservative scientist as well as the uninformed layman. The term literally commanded respect, but, as with so many phrases in our language, it has lost its impact and instills little more emotion than an amber light at a traffic intersection. This deflation process has been catalyzed by articles in popular lay magazines and the widespread use of these materials as insecticides. Unfortunately, the compounds themselves have not lost their toxicity.

During the war years, the German government devoted vast expenditures of money to the development of these compounds as potential antipersonnel agents. Many of the compounds synthesized are among the most lethal chemicals ever discovered. Published reports show lethal doses as low as 20 μg./Kg. for rats. In view of the indications that man is many times more sensitive than the rodent, they should be reasonably good antipersonnel agents.

Shortly after the war, these poisons logically found their way into European and American industry as insecticides. Years of screening have separated a series of compounds that can be safely manufactured and are effective insecticides. Their lethal dose in rodents ranges upward from 1 mg./Kg., but their mechanism of action remains the same—inhibition of the enzyme cholinesterase. Without this enzyme, an accumulation of the chemical mediator acetyl choline occurs, causing convulsions, respiratory arrest, and death.

Many deaths resulted from accidental poisoning during the first few years that these compounds were released for insecticidal use, but with experience the manufacturers and physicians learned to save a large percentage of these accidentally poisoned individuals through the proper use of atropine.

But this was only part of the fear of the Food and Drug Administration. This new insecticidal use engendered the contamination of food with all of its long-range implications. Could these compounds be used as insecticides without inflicting any additional biologic stress on the unsuspecting consumer? To answer this question, the Food and Drug Administration and the manufacturers conducted two year feeding studies in laboratory animals. Throughout the experiments the animals appeared normal, and at autopsy gross and microscopic tissue changes were absent. Mortality occurred only when the daily dosage approached the single lethal dose. It was difficult to avoid a conclusion that these compounds were not cumulative poisons. In 1950, this was almost a universal opinion, and the fear of continuous ingestion of small quantities was waning.

However, just as death is a very crude end point, so pathologic changes are an incomplete end point. For this reason, the Food and Drug Administration continued its investigations by searching out the enzyme changes that might reveal cumulative toxicity at small dosages. Here the changes were dramatic. As little as 0.1 parts per million in the diet or 1/1000 of the single lethal dose with some compounds could produce significant inhibition of the cholinesterase enzyme.

Thus, every insecticide currently used has been screened by the Food and Drug Administration or by the manufacturer for these effects. Several have been found to be too toxic for insecticidal use, while others have been permitted where the residue remaining at harvest is sufficiently below the level that might cause such enzyme inhibition.

The "nerve poisons" have found a useful place in the agricultural industry.

However, our familiarity with them over the years should not have bred contempt, but rather even greater respect. They are not only acute poisons, but cumulative ones as well. Therefore, to maintain our food supply free from deleterious levels of poisonous chemicals, it is necessary to demonstrate the type and degree of cumulative toxicity. It is the responsibility of the Food and Drug Administration to see that safety is adequately demonstrated before general use is undertaken, and this responsibility is not taken lightly.

INDEX

AUTHOR INDEX

SUBJECT INDEX

140